POOLEYS

Private Pilots Guide

JAR

Flight Performance
& Planning

David Cockburn

Nothing in this syllabus supersedes any legislation, rules, regulations or procedures contained in any operational document issued by Her Majesty's Stationery Office, the Civil Aviation Authority, the Joint Aviation Authorities, ICAO, the manufacturers of aircraft, engines and systems, or by the operators of aircraft throughout the world.

JAR Flight Performance and Planning

© David Cockburn 2004

ISBN 1-84336-057-8

Pooleys Flight Equipment Ltd
Elstree Aerodrome
Hertfordshire
WD6 3AW
England

Tel: 0208 953 4870
Fax: 0208 953 2512
www.pooleys.com

Preface

This book, the second in the series, has been produced primarily to assist an applicant for a Private Pilot's Licence in the study for the Flight Performance and Planning examination. It is not intended as a complete course of study, but is designed to act as a guide to the main points in the syllabus. However, it is also intended to help those who have already passed the examination by giving them a document to which they can refer in order to achieve safe and practical flight planning.

The most important parts, especially those relating directly to safety, are covered in detail. However, the coverage of parts which the author considers less vital is only sufficient to give a basic understanding of general structure, sufficient to obtain a pass in the examinations. To cover the whole syllabus, or indeed to fly with a high level of safety, more detailed knowledge is required, and pilots should strive to learn as much about their aircraft and its environment as possible. Pilots must refer to the Flight Manual and other documents for accuracy and confirmation before flight.

This is especially true because this document is not normally amended as legislation changes. However, this book has been updated to reflect changes in information published in the AIC on "Take-off, climb and landing performance of light aeroplanes" in September 2002.

In this book, the male pronoun 'he' is often used to refer to both genders. This is no slight on the ladies who fly, merely a space saving and readability measure.

Comments or suggestions on this or any other guides in this series are welcomed.

Editorial Team

AUTHOR David Cockburn

David Cockburn served for many years in the Royal Air Force as a pilot and flying instructor, amassing nearly 6000 flying hours including over 1000 hours instructing on jet trainers and 1000 hours on light piston aeroplanes. During that time he specialised in teaching mainly visual navigation techniques to pilots and navigators in the air and on the ground. He holds a UK Airline Transport Pilots Licence, and since leaving the RAF has worked as a ground instructor in professional flying training schools in this country and abroad, and is the author of several professional training books and manuals. He continues to give flying instruction at flying clubs to PPL and IMC rating students.

Having decided to concentrate on private pilot training, it became apparent that students and private pilots found it difficult to find the practical and important information they needed from the detailed descriptions in the available textbooks. He has therefore produced these guides to provide this practical and important information.

Daljeet Gill

Daljeet is Head of Design & Development for Pooleys Flight Equipment and editor of the Pooleys Private Pilots Guides, Pre-flight Briefing, R/T Communications, Pooleys ATPL Manuals and Air Presentation, Ground School Training Transparencies plus many others. Daljeet has been involved with editing, typesetting and design for all these publications. Graduated in 1999 with a BA (hons) in Graphic Design, she deals with marketing, advertising & design of our new products. She maintains our website and produces our Pooleys Catalogue annually.

Contents

Intentionally Left Blank

Chapter 1

Mass and its Distribution

1.1 Introduction

One of the responsibilities of a pilot is the safe loading of his aircraft, both in terms of the total mass of the aircraft, and its safe distribution. In this chapter we discuss the reasons why this is so important, and look at some of the results of incorrect loading.

1.2 Mass

Every object has **mass**. In daily life we usually refer to an object's **weight**, but strictly speaking, "weight" is the force that is exerted on the mass by the Earth's gravity. Examinations, legal documents, and this book also, will appear to interchange the terms, but it is wise to remember that they are not strictly synonymous.

1.3 Reasons for Limiting Mass

The total mass of an aircraft must be restricted for several reasons. The force exerted by the aircraft through its undercarriage onto the runway or taxiway, may damage that surface. The force on the aircraft structure at the top of the undercarriage legs, or as transferred from them to the wing/fuselage junction through the rest of the structure, may cause damage to the aircraft. It is worth remembering that although a force may appear to have caused no damage when it has been applied, it will have produced movement of the structure which will reduce the structure's ability to withstand such forces in the future (this is called "fatigue"). A limitation on "**ramp**" mass is usually for this reason.

Landing mass is also limited for structural reasons, but is usually lower than ramp mass because of the extra force required to stop the aircraft descending. Another reason for limiting landing mass is that the energy required to stop the aircraft from flying speed depends on the product of the mass and the square of the landing groundspeed, and that energy must be absorbed by the aircraft's brakes. That same reason may limit the **takeoff** mass, because if an emergency occurs the aircraft may have to stop from high speed.

Another reason for limiting takeoff mass, usually in larger aircraft, is the sheer ability for the aircraft's wings to lift the aircraft off the ground and climb over obstructions. In order for the aircraft to fly, the weight exerted by the earth's gravity must be balanced by the lift generated by the wings. This lift depends on the air density, the true air speed, the wing area, and the angle of attack. Density depends on temperature and pressure, which can be measured as pressure altitude. This means the mass is limited by altitude and temperature factors, so Weight, Altitude and Temperature are interdependent. We call the resulting limits **"WAT"** limits. Landing will also have WAT limits, because of the need to climb away safely on a go-around.

Even in cruising flight, excess mass will reduce performance and manoeuvrability, increase fuel consumption, reduce range and increase stalling speed. If one engine fails in a multi-engined aeroplane, the excess mass may reduce performance to such an extent that the aircraft may not be able to climb above the terrain.

Structural loads on the aircraft are also caused by the bending moments from the weight of the fuselage against the wings. Excess bending causes fatigue and possible subsequent failure in the structure. In some aircraft, much of the fuel is kept in the wings, and the weight of fuel counters these bending moments. Without that fuel (for example on landing), the mass of the fuselage may have to be limited in some cases. This is given as a limited **"Zero Fuel Mass"**.

Limits are listed in Flight Manuals. These will be the most critical limits, usually for structural reasons, but the other disadvantages will still exist.

1.4   Effects of Excess Mass

To summarise, if an aircraft mass is too great, it will produce some or all of the following effects.

    a. **REDUCED PERFORMANCE**
            Reduced rate of climb,
                ceiling, manoeuvrability,
            Increased fuel consumption,
                stalling speed,
            Reduced range.

    b. **INCREASED WEAR**
            On tyres and brakes.

    c. **STRUCTURAL DAMAGE**
            Immediate or fatigue damage.

1.5   Mass Distribution

The way the mass is distributed along the longitudinal axis of the aircraft is also important. An object can be said to have a "centre of gravity", where it can be balanced, as seen later. Every aircraft has an ideal position for its centre of gravity. If the centre of gravity is not in the ideal position, the aircraft's **performance** will reduce. As the centre of gravity moves further away from the ideal, **stability** and **handling** deteriorate also, and beyond certain limits they may become unacceptable. The position of the aircraft's loaded centre of gravity is therefore limited.

If the centre of gravity of the aircraft falls behind the main undercarriage of an aircraft with a nosewheel, the tail will hit the ground. This is obviously a limitation on centre of gravity (C of G) position, and there will probably be a similar limitation on the forward position of the C of G, in that excess weight on the nosewheel may cause damage to it or the structure around it. However, these are not usually the limiting factors.

The forces acting on an aircraft are Lift, Weight, Thrust, and Drag. Looking purely at Lift and Weight, as shown in fig 1.1, we can consider that the Weight acts through the C of G, and the Lift can be said to act through a 'centre of lift'. If the centre of gravity is not coincident with the centre of lift (in this case behind it) there will be a 'couple' from the two forces attempting to pitch the aircraft nose (in this case upwards). The couple between Thrust and Drag may either increase or reduce that pitching moment, but we shall disregard their effect here, although pilots will feel their effect as a trim change when applying or reducing power.

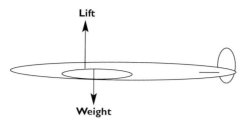

Lift

Weight

FIG 1.1 PITCHING MOMENT

The pitching moment must be compensated by a lift force on the tailplane, as shown in fig 1.2. In addition to the profile drag from the shape of the tailplane, this lift force will produce **induced** drag (see chapter 11), which will reduce performance.

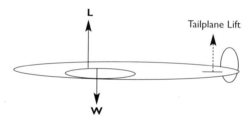

L

Tailplane Lift

W

FIG 1.2 TAILPLANE LIFT

As the centre of gravity moves further away from the ideal, the lift and induced drag (which we call "trim drag") from the tailplane will increase, and performance will decrease.

In the case considered here, lift from the tailplane must compensate for the rearward C of G. If the aircraft is designed for that position of the C of G, that lift can be provided by the shape and angle of incidence of the tailplane. If however that C of G position has not been designed for, the extra lift must come from the elevator, or changed tailplane incidence in the case of an all-flying tail. There is a limit to the amount of extra lift obtained by control deflection; beyond that, the aircraft will be uncontrollable. Before that happens, control effectiveness will reduce progressively, causing problems when avoiding or recovering from a stall. The same effect will occur in reverse if the lift from the tailplane is required to act downwards, for example during the roundout to land the aircraft.

We have looked at the reduction in control effectiveness as the C of G moves away from the ideal position. The stability of the aircraft will also be affected. The tailplane's primary function is to produce a "restoring moment" if the aircraft pitches in turbulence, bringing the aircraft back to the pitch attitude from which it started. As the C of G moves forward, aircraft stability increases; the restoring moment from the tailplane increases with distance from the C of G, producing high control forces. The reverse will happen as the C of G moves aft, encouraging overcontrolling, especially at slow speeds such as during the roundout or on takeoff.

1.6   Effects of Forward C of G

To summarise, if the mass of the aircraft is distributed forward of the ideal position, there will be the following consequences:

a. **TRIM DRAG**
   More thrust needed for a given speed, so reduced range.

b. **INCREASED STABILITY**
   More effort to manoeuvre the aircraft.

c. **REDUCED CONTROL**
   Difficulty in raising the nose, especially on roundout.

1.7   Effect of Aft C of G

If the mass is distributed rearward, making the C of G position behind the ideal, the effects will be as follows:

a. **TRIM DRAG**
   More thrust needed for a given speed, so reduced range

b. **REDUCED STABILITY**
   Possible overcontrol, especially during roundout.

c. **REDUCED CONTROL**
   Difficulty in stall recovery, possible nose lift on takeoff.

1.8   Internal Load Distribution

An aircraft is designed to carry a load, either freight or passengers. The amount and position of that load is important; we have seen the general effects of excess or incorrectly distributed mass. However, there are other considerations. Firstly, any load inside the aircraft must have its weight supported so that it does not cause damage to the aircraft structure; some parts of aircraft floors may be able to support greater loads than others. In addition, the load, whether freight or human, must not be able to move, especially during phases of flight when the position of the centre of gravity is critical, such as takeoff or landing. Freight must be tied down securely, and passengers restrained by belts. Apart from C of G problems, of course, incorrectly secured loads may move in turbulence or a crash situation and cause increased damage or injury to persons.

1.9   Centre of Gravity Limits

To avoid problems caused by the position of the centre of gravity being too far forward or aft, the manufacturer has tested his aircraft, and calculated the furthest **forward** and furthest **aft** position of the centre of gravity which will allow safe flight. These are published in flight and operating manuals, and the commander is responsible for ensuring that the aircraft is loaded to comply with these limits. If, after loading, it is discovered that the position of the C of G is outside these limits, the distribution of the load must be changed. However, the pilot must be aware that, even if the C of G position is within the prescribed limits, his aircraft's handling may be affected as discussed above, albeit to an extent which the manufacturer and certificating authority considers safe. The position of the C of G will change as fuel is consumed, and perhaps as parachutists are dropped. In any event, the C of G must be kept inside the limits **at all times.**

1.   Which of the following is not a likely result of overloading the aircraft?

     a.   Reduced range
     b.   Brake failure on landing
     c.   Difficulty in stall recovery
     d.   Increased tyre wear

2.   Which of the following is a likely result of flying an aircraft with a C of G position forward of the ideal?

     a.   Reduced range
     b.   Brake failure on landing
     c.   Difficulty in stall recovery
     d.   Increased tyre wear

3.   Which of the following is not a possible result of the aircraft's C of G being too far aft?

     a.   Reduced range
     b.   Difficulty in stall avoidance
     c.   Overcontrol on takeoff
     d.   Difficulty in roundout

4.   Which of the following is a possible cause of increased fuel consumption?

     a.   Excess aircraft mass
     b.   C of G position too far forward
     c.   C of G position too far aft
     d.   All of the above

5.   Which of the following is a possible cause of overcontrol on roundout?

     a.   Excess aircraft mass
     b.   C of G position too far forward
     c.   C of G position too far aft
     d.   All of the above

6. Which of the following is a possible cause of a landing aircraft overrunning the runway?

    a. Excess aircraft mass
    b. C of G position too far forward
    c. C of G position too far aft
    d. All of the above

7. Why must the load of an aircraft be properly secured on takeoff?

    a. To prevent damage in the event of an accident
    b. To avoid unwanted movement of the centre of gravity
    c. Both (a) and (b)
    d. Neither (a) nor (b)

8. What does "WAT" stand for in "WAT limits"?

    a. Weight, Aerodrome and Takeoff
    b. Wings, Airframe and Trim
    c. Weight, Altitude and Takeoff
    d. Weight, Altitude and Temperature

Chapter 2

Load Definitions

2.1 Introduction

When talking about loading, there are many items which may be limited, so we should understand exactly what is meant by each limitation. There are strict definitions, some of which you must know. This chapter will list and describe the most important.

2.2 C of G Definitions

a. CENTRE OF GRAVITY
The point where a body's mass is said to be concentrated.
The point where the weight of a body can be said to act.

b. CENTRE OF LIFT
The point where the lift from the wings can be said to act.

c. DATUM POINT
The point from which the position of the C of G is measured.
This is defined for each aircraft type.

2.3 Initial Mass Definitions

a. EMPTY WEIGHT OR EMPTY MASS
The weight or mass of an aircraft as measured, without equipment, fuel or oil.

b. BASIC EQUIPMENT
All items fitted to an aircraft and remaining in it, including non-consumable fluids (hydraulic oil, unusable fuel and oil).

c. **BASIC OPERATING WEIGHT OR MASS**

Empty Weight/Mass plus Basic Equipment. This, and **Basic C of G position**, is measured by weighing and written in the weight schedule. This is the usual start point for load calculations, and is sometimes incorrectly called the aircraft prepared for service (APS) mass. APS mass correctly applies to commercial operations, and includes the crew.

d. **LOAD**

Anything placed in the aircraft above the basic operating mass. For a light aircraft, this includes the crew, baggage, passengers, and usable fuel.

e. **GROSS WEIGHT OR GROSS MASS**

The total weight/mass of the aircraft and its contents at a particular time

f. **WEIGHT SCHEDULE**

Part of the Certificate of Airworthiness. Kept for 6 months after the **next** weighing.

2.4 Weight Calculation Definitions

a. **MAXIMUM AUTHORISED MASS** (or Weight)

The maximum mass for a particular phase of flight permitted by the C of A.

b. **ZERO FUEL MASS** (Weight)

The Actual Mass minus the usable fuel. The maximum authorised zero fuel mass is often expressed as **MZFM.**

c. **TAKEOFF MASS** (Weight)

The actual mass of the aircraft at the start of the takeoff roll. The maximum authorised takeoff mass is often expressed as **MTMA**

d. **RAMP MASS** (Weight)

The Takeoff Mass plus fuel used for start-up and taxi. The maximum authorised ramp mass can be expressed as **MRMA**

e. **LANDING MASS** (Weight)

The mass of the aircraft at touchdown. The maximum authorised landing mass can be expressed as **MLMA**

2.5   Measurement of C of G Position

The position of the aircraft's basic centre of gravity along its longitudinal axis (a straight line joining the nose to the tail) is measured by weighing and written in the weight schedule, which is part of the aircraft's Certificate of Airworthiness. The C of G position is usually written as a distance from the Datum Point, which can be at any point along that longitudinal axis, but is defined by the manufacturer for each aircraft type. The Datum Point is often at the nose, but may be at the point where the wing leading edge joins the fuselage, or at the bulkhead where the engine meets the cockpit. The C of G position may be marked positive (+) if it is aft of the datum, which is almost invariably the case with a light aeroplane.

2.6   Mass of Fuel etc.

Fuel and other liquids are measured by volume, in units such as litres, 'imperial' gallons, or US gallons (1.2 US gallons = 1 imperial [British]gallon). Fuel mass calculations use units such as kilograms or pounds. To convert from volume to mass, liquids are compared to water, because the definitions of mass units involve a certain amount of water. One litre of water has a mass of one kilogram. One imperial gallon of water has a weight of ten pounds. Comparing fuel or oil to water we refer to their 'specific gravity' or SG, which is the volume of water which weighs the same as one unit volume of the fuel. Unfortunately, SG varies with temperature! However, most calculations will use a standard SG which is the SG at 15°C (approximately 0.72 for AVGAS).

One litre of fuel with a SG of 0.72 will have a mass of 0.72 kg - 10 litres has a mass of 7.2 kg
One (imperial) gallon of fuel with a SG of 0.72 will weigh 7.2 pounds
One US gallon of fuel with a SG of 0.72 will weigh 7.2/1.2 = 6 pounds
many flight handbooks of American built aircraft actually give a standard weight of fuel , such as 6 pounds per US gallon, but may refer to that figure as the SG.   Examination questions may be complicated by mixing units between imperial, US, and metric.
Read the question carefully!
One imperial gallon = 1.2 US gallons = 4.55 litres.
One kilogram equates to 2.2 pounds

Intentionally Left Blank

1. What is defined as "The mass of an aircraft as measured, without any equipment, fuel or oil"?

   a. Basic equipment
   b. Basic Operating Mass
   c. Zero Fuel Mass
   d. Empty Mass

2. What is defined as " The maximum mass of an aircraft at the start of its takeoff roll, as permitted by the Civil Aviation Authority"?

   a. The Takeoff Mass
   b. MRMA
   c. MTMA
   d. MLMA

3. Which of a, b, and c is different from the others?

   a. The Actual Mass minus the usable fuel
   b. The Basic Operating Mass plus the Load
   c. The Zero Fuel Mass
   d. They are all the same

4. Which of the following is "The maximum Basic Operating Mass plus Load authorised at the commencement of the takeoff roll, plus fuel used during start-up and taxi"

   a. MRMA
   b. MLMA
   c. MTMA
   d. Actual Mass

5. What is defined as "The point from which all calculations with regard to the position where the mass of a body can be said to act are measured"?

   a. The Centre of Lift
   b. The Mean Aerodynamic Chord
   c. The Centre of Gravity
   d. The Datum Point

6. Which of the following is the 'gross weight' of an aircraft?

    a. The weight of the aircraft without fuel, crew or load
    b. The maximum landing weight authorised
    c. The weight of the aircraft with crew and disposable load but without fuel
    d. The actual total weight of the aircraft and its contents at a particular time

7. What is the weight of 120 US gallons of fuel with a specific gravity of 0.72?

    a.   60 pounds
    b.   72 pounds
    c. 720 pounds
    d. 864 pounds

8. What is the weight of 200 litres of fuel with a specific gravity of 0.725?

    a.   145 pounds
    b.   240 pounds
    c. 1220 pounds
    d. 1450 pounds

Chapter 3

Loading Legislation

3.1 Introduction

There are many laws relating to the loading of aircraft, and the relevant ones for private pilots are contained in the Air Navigation Order (ANO). This short chapter guides you through these.

3.2 Basic Mass and C of G Calculation

The rules for weighing aircraft and calculating basic mass and C of G position are contained in the ANO article 18. It actually states "Every flying machine must be weighed, and its centre of gravity determined, as required by the CAA", which is rather nebulous, but means that it must happen before a C of A is issued. The **operator** (usually the owner) is responsible for preparing the weight schedule which shows the basic mass and position of the basic C of G, and that schedule must be kept, not only until the next weighing and schedule preparation, but for a further 6 months. Any engineering work carried out must also have a certificate of re-weighing, or a certificate that such re-weighing is not necessary, signed by a licensed engineer, as part of the **Certificate of Release to Service** required before the aircraft flies again.

3.3 Loading

ANO article 43 (d) lays down that the commander of an aircraft must satisfy himself before flight 'that the load carried by the aircraft is of such weight, and is so distributed and secured, that it may safely be carried on the intended flight'. It means that the commander (pilot) must satisfy himself that the aircraft weight and balance are within the limits set by the C of A. To be sure, he should complete a "load sheet" like his commercial cousins, and flight manuals include forms which can be used for this purpose. Later chapters describe how to use different types of form.

3.7 Exercise

1. How long must an operator keep the weight schedule?

   a. 6 months after the weighing
   b. 6 months after the signature of the C of A
   c. 6 months after the next weight schedule is completed
   d. 6 months after the flight takes off

2. Which of the following must be shown on a weight schedule?

   a. The aircraft's basic mass and C of G position as measured
   b. The APS mass as assumed for the route
   c. The position of the aircraft's C of G at MTMA
   d. A certificate that re-weighing is not required

Chapter 4

Tabular Load Calculations

4.1 Introduction

The commander has no responsibilities concerning the weight schedule, but he is directly responsible for the safety of the aircraft, in other words that the aircraft as loaded complies with the C of A., as required by ANO article 43. This chapter introduces the tabular method (as used in many flight manuals) of calculating the position of an aircraft's centre of gravity from the Basic Mass and C of G position, and the masses and positions of individual items of the load.

4.2 Theory

The centre of gravity of an object can be defined as "the point through which the weight of the object can be said to act". That means that whichever position the object is placed in, if one supports the object exactly underneath its C of G, it will balance. We could use trial and error to find the C of G position by attempting to balance the aircraft on various points, but it is much easier to use mathematics!

We do not normally concern ourselves with the lateral (sideways) position of the C of G, as it varies little from the aircraft centreline unless there is a great fuel imbalance. We are more concerned with its longitudinal position, and we can represent the side view of an aircraft with a long beam, as in fig. 4.1. If the beam (aircraft) is balanced, then the C of G is above the pivot.

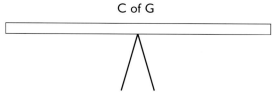

FIG 4.1 EVEN BEAM

A perfect beam made of one material, and of the same width and cross section throughout, would balance at the mid-point, as in fig 4.1. However, the mass of the parts of the beam may not be equally distributed, just as the masses of items inside an aircraft will not be. If we consider all the masses of different parts of the beam as being the same as actual masses hanging from it, the picture may change to something like fig. 4.2. However, just as on a beam balance used for weighing, the weight of the item on the left of the pivot multiplied by its distance from the C of G (its "**moment**") will equal the **moment** of the weight on the right of the pivot. Each moment in this case will be **24** pound inches.

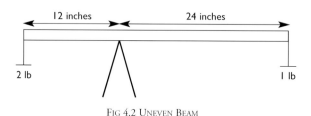

FIG 4.2 UNEVEN BEAM

The C of G is the point where the weight of the beam can be said to act, that is above the pivot. By Newton's 3rd law (every action has an equal and opposite reaction), we can say that in Fig 4.2, there are 3 forces acting on the beam in 3 different places. A force of 2 lb weight acts downwards at the left end of the beam, a force of 1 lb weight acts downwards at the right end of the beam, and a balancing force of 3 lb weight acts upwards at the C of G.

These forces are in balance (up and down), and their moments are also in balance around the C of G. We measure moments as torques attempting to rotate the beam. In this case if we measure around the C of G, a torque of 24 lb in is attempting to rotate the beam clockwise, and an equal torque of 24 lb in is attempting to rotate it anticlockwise. However, from basic mathematics, if the beam is in equilibrium (not accelerating in any direction), we can measure these moments from any point, and the sum of all the torques trying to rotate it clockwise will equal the sum of all the torques trying to rotate it anticlockwise. In fig. 4.2, if we measure the moments from the left end of the beam, there will be a force of 1 lb acting 36 inches from the point of measurement (the Datum), giving a torque of 36 lb in acting clockwise. There will also be a force at the C of G (the reaction) of a total of 3 lb acting at 12 inches making a torque of 36 lb in trying to rotate the beam clockwise. The torques are balanced, and the beam is in equilibrium.

This type of calculation can be used if we do not know the position of the C of G. If we only know the weights at each end of the beam (2 lb at the left end, 1 lb at the right end), and we know the distances involved, we can continue to use our Datum of the left end of the beam. We know that a force of 1 lb, acting at 36 inches from the datum, is trying to turn the beam clockwise, giving a clockwise moment of 36 lb in. The total weight of the beam is 3 lb, and the reaction to that total weight acts through the C of G to oppose the clockwise moment. That reacting moment must also be 36 lb in, and the force is 3 lb, so the distance from the datum to the C of G must be (36 divided by 3 =) **12** inches to the right of the datum.

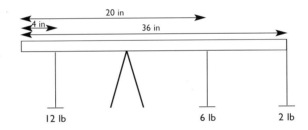

FIG 4.3 FINDING THE C OF G POSITION

In fig 4.3, we have a beam with weights positioned as shown. We wish to find the position of the centre of gravity. The total weight on the beam is 20 lb, so the reaction through the C of G must be 20 lb. If we use a datum of the left end of the beam, the total clockwise moments equal (4 x 12) + (20 x 6) + (36 x 2) lb in, so the anticlockwise balancing moment through the C of G also equals 240 lb in. The total reaction is 20 lb, so the arm of the anticlockwise moment (the distance from the datum) must equal 240÷20 = **12** in. The Centre of Gravity is therefore 12 inches from the datum.

4.3 Aircraft C of G Calculations

This principle is used to find the centre of gravity of an aircraft. All the moments attempting to pitch the aircraft nose upwards from the datum (clockwise if the nose is to the left) must be balanced by the moment of the reaction to the total weight multiplied by the distance of the C of G aft from the datum. As a formula, the distance of the C of G from the datum can be expressed as:

$$\frac{W1.D1 + W2.D2 + W3.D3 + W4.D4 + W5.D5 + W6.D6 + W7.D7 + W8.D8 \text{ etc}}{W1 + W2 + W3 + W4 + W5 + W6 + W7 + W8 \text{ etc}}$$

Where W1, W2 etc. are the individual weights of items, and D1, D2 etc. are their respective distances from the datum.

For example, if we measure the weights of all the component items of an aircraft and its load, and their positions as distances aft of the datum, in a table such as at fig 4.4, we can calculate the position of the C of G quite simply, using our formula.

Item	Weight (lb)	Arm (in)	Moment (lb in)
A/C Basic Mass	2500	64	
Crew	200	40	
Cargo	1500	78	
Fuel	300	40	
Total			

Fig 4.4 Sample Form

In fig 4.5, we can fill in the total weight as 4500 lb, and each moment as 160000, 8000, 117000, and 12000 lb in. Add up the total moments to reach a total of 297000, which we divide by the total weight of 4500, to produce a result of 66, which is the distance in inches of our C of G aft of the datum.

Item	Weight (lb)	Arm (in)	Moment (lb in)
A/C Basic Mass	2500	64	160000
Crew	200	40	8000
Cargo	1500	78	117000
Fuel	300	40	297000
Total	4500		

$$\text{C of G position} = \frac{297000}{4500} = \textbf{66 inches aft of datum}$$

Fig 4.5 Calculation

4.4 Complex Calculations

In the previous example we only considered a datum position where all the mass lay aft of it. Different aircraft may have a datum in a position where some of the masses lie forward of the datum, and attempt to rotate the aircraft nose down. In calculations, we simply count these moments as "**negative**", and subtract them from the total of "**positive**" moments before dividing the result by the total mass.

Fig 4.6 is an example of a C of G calculation table with a datum aft of the nose. A similar table is found in the flight manual or operating manual of most light aircraft. It should be completed before every flight.

LOADING FORM

Maximum Takeoff Mass Authorised: 2400 lb
Maximum Landing Mass Authorised: 2300 lb
Centre of Gravity Limits: 18 to 22 inches aft of datum

Item	Weight (lb)	Arm (in)	+ve moment	-ve moment
Basic Mass	1396	+ 28		
Crew & Front Passenger		- 6		
Oil (SG .8)		- 18		
Rear Passengers		+ 24		
Baggage		+ 44		
Fuel (SG .72)		+ 20		
Total				

FIG 4.6 LOADING FORM

The form is almost self - explanatory. The person completing the form (usually the pilot) simply fills in the relevant boxes. For example, if this aircraft is loaded with pilot and 1 front seat passenger, together weighing 330 lb, and 2 passengers in the rear seats, together weighing 340 lb, with total baggage in the baggage compartment of 36 lb, and 2 gallons of oil and 39 gallons of fuel, we should fill in the form as at fig 4.7. (1 imperial gallon of fuel with specific gravity of .72 weighs 7.2 lb, but many aircraft use US gallons, weighing about 6 lb at normal temperatures.)

LOADING FORM

Maximum Takeoff Mass Authorised: 2400 lb
Maximum Landing Mass Authorised: 2300 lb
Centre of Gravity Limits: 18 to 22 inches aft of datum

Item	Weight (lb)	Arm (in)	+ve moment	-ve moment
Basic Mass	1396	+ 28	+ 39088	
Crew & Front Passenger	330	- 6		- 1980
Oil (SG .8)	16	- 18		- 288
Rear Passengers	340	+ 24	+ 8160	
Baggage	36	+ 44	+ 1584	
Fuel (SG .72)	280.8	+ 20	+ 5616	
Total	2398.8		+ 54448	- 2268
			- 2268	
			+ 52180	

FIG 4.7 LOADING FORM COMPLETED FOR TAKEOFF

The total mass is within limits for takeoff at **2398.8 lb**. To find the C of G position, we have subtracted the total negative moments from the total positive moments to arrive at an overall total moment of + 52180 lb in. To find the actual position of the C of G as loaded for takeoff, we must divide that overall total moment by the total weight, producing a figure of: $\dfrac{52180}{2398.8}$ = **21.75** inches aft of Datum, which is within limits.

4.5   Landing Calculations

However, these figures are only valid for takeoff. The aircraft must also be within limits when it lands, so a further calculation is required at the expected masses of the aircraft and its loads at the expected landing time. The simplest way of achieving that is to complete a further loading form with the new expected masses. Fig 4.8 shows the calculations for landing if the aircraft has used 29 gallons of fuel and $1/2$ gallon of oil during its flight.

LOADING FORM

Maximum Takeoff Mass Authorised: 2400 lb
Maximum Landing Mass Authorised: 2300 lb
Centre of Gravity Limits: 18 to 22 inches aft of datum

Item	Weight (lb)	Arm (in)	+ve moment	-ve moment
Basic Mass	1396	+ 28	+ 39088	
Crew & Front Passenger	330	- 6		- 1980
Oil (SG .8)	12	- 18		- 216
Rear Passengers	340	+ 24	+ 8160	
Baggage	36	+ 44	+ 1584	
Fuel (SG .72)	72	+ 20	+ 1440	
Total	2186		+ 50272	- 2196
			- 2196	
			+ 48076	

FIG. 4.8 COMPLETED FORM FOR LANDING

The figures for landing are a mass of **2186 lb**, well within limits, and a moment of + 48076, producing a landing C of G position of 21.993 inches aft of datum, which again is within limits, if only just. (A sensible pilot will be ready for any possible problems caused by an aft C of G).

4.6 Alternate Landing Calculations

To save time, it is possible to re-calculate for landing without completing another copy of the loading form. Starting with the takeoff calculations, we can proceed as follows.

Mass of fuel used	= 208.8 lb	Moment of fuel used	= + 4176
Mass of oil used	= 4	Moment of oil used	= - 72
Total weight used	= 212.8	Total moment used	= + 4104

Takeoff mass	= 2398.8	Takeoff moment	= +52180
- Total mass used	= 212.8	- Total moment used	(+)4104
Landing Mass	2186	Landing Moment	48076

Again divide the moment by the weight to find the landing C of G position of **21.993** in aft. This method is quicker than the total re-calculation, but if you have doubts about your maths, it may be safer, if more time consuming, to use a second copy of the form. In an examination, however, you may not have the original form, so practise this method.

4.7   Exercise

1.   Using the form below, calculate the total weight and the position of the C of G for takeoff of the aircraft with loads as follows: Pilot weight 165 lb; front seat passenger weight 165 lb; rear seat passenger weight 190 lb; baggage weight 70 lb; fuel load 37 gallons; oil 3 gallons.

LOADING FORM

Maximum Takeoff Mass Authorised: 2400 lb
Maximum Landing Mass Authorised: 2300 lb
Centre of Gravity Limits: 18 to 22 inches aft of datum

Item	Weight (lb)	Arm (in)	+ve moment	-ve moment
Basic Mass	1396	+ 28		
Crew & Front Passenger		- 6		
Oil (SG .8)		- 18		
Rear Passengers		+ 24		
Baggage .		+ 44		
Fuel (SG .72)		+ 20		
Total				

2.   Is the aircraft in question 1 loaded safely?

   a.   Yes
   b.   No, the takeoff mass is above authorised limits
   c.   No, the position of the centre of gravity is outside limits
   d.   No, both the mass and C of G position are outside limits

3.   If the aircraft in question 1 uses 20 gallons of fuel and $\frac{1}{2}$ gallon of oil enroute, calculate the landing mass and C of G position using the alternate method.

4.   Use the form provided to calculate the landing mass and C of G position.

LOADING FORM

Maximum Takeoff Mass Authorised: 2400 lb
Maximum Landing Mass Authorised: 2300 lb
Centre of Gravity Limits: 18 to 22 inches aft of datum

Item	Weight (lb)	Arm (in)	+ve moment	-ve moment
Basic Mass	1396	+ 28		
Crew & Front Passenger		- 6		
Oil (SG .8)		- 18		
Rear Passengers		+ 24		
Baggage		+ 44		
Fuel (SG .72)		+ 20		
Total				

5.   Is this aircraft loaded safely for landing?

6.   An aircraft's take-off weight is 2300 lb, and its C of G position is 21 inches aft of datum. If it uses 30 gallons of fuel at 6 lb per gallon from a position 10 inches aft of datum, what will be the position of the C of G on landing?

Intentionally Left Blank

Chapter 5

Amending the C of G Position

5.1 Introduction

We can now calculate the position of an aircraft's C of G. However, if that position is outside the limits, the aircraft cannot be allowed to take off; we must be able to change that C of G position to bring it back inside the limits. This chapter considers simple methods of moving loads to produce a C of G position within limits.

5.2 Initial Calculation

Let us look at the calculation below:.

LOADING FORM

Maximum Takeoff Mass Authorised: 2400 lb
Maximum Landing Mass Authorised: 2300 lb
Centre of Gravity Limits: 18 to 22 inches aft of datum

Item	**Weight** (lb)	**Arm** (in)	**+ve** moment	**-ve** moment
Basic Mass	1396	+ 28	+ 39088	
Crew & Front Passenger	330	- 6		- 1860
Oil (SG .8)	24	- 18		- 432
Rear Passengers	190	+ 24	+ 4560	
Baggage	80	+ 44	+ 3520	
Fuel (SG .72)	266.4	+ 20	+ 5328	
Total	2266.4		+ 52496	- 2292
			- 2292	
			+ 50204	

Position of C of G = $\dfrac{50204}{2266.4}$ = **22.15** in aft of datum.

The aircraft C of G is outside limits. Some part of the load must be changed. Of course, it is possible to take some out, which would be necessary if the actual mass were above the maximum authorised mass for the phase of flight. However, we do not normally want to disappoint our passengers, so it is better to move the load rather than reduce it.

5.3 Simple Movement

We may have to decide whether moving a particular part of the load from one place to another will bring the C of G position within limits. In that case, we can treat the calculation in a similar fashion to that of a changing fuel load. The simple, but long, method would be to recalculate the load sheet with the new figures. As an example, let us decide whether moving the baggage from the baggage compartment to the rear seat would allow a safe takeoff.

LOADING FORM

Maximum Takeoff Mass Authorised: 2400 lb
Maximum Landing Mass Authorised: 2300 lb
Centre of Gravity Limits: 18 to 22 inches aft of datum

Item	Weight (lb)	Arm (in)	+ve moment	-ve moment
Basic Mass	1396	+ 28	+ 39088	
Crew & Front Passenger	310	- 6		- 1860
Oil (SG .8)	24	- 18		- 432
Rear Passengers	270	+ 24	+ 6480	
Baggage		+ 44		
Fuel (SG .72)	266.4	+ 20	+ 5328	
Total	2266.4		+ 50896	- 2292
			- 2292	
			+ 48604	

New of C of G $= \dfrac{48604}{2266.4} =$ **21.45** in aft of datum.

This is within limits, so the movement would produce the desired effect.

Alternatively, we could use the alternate method for finding the landing C of G position, as in the previous chapter. If we really do move part of the load, we first remove it from its original position then place it in its new position. We can use that principle in calculations as follows.

Moment of load being removed	=	80 x + 44 =	+ 3520
Moment of load being replaced	=	80 x + 24 =	+ 1920
Reduction in takeoff moment	=		+ 1600

New takeoff moment = original - reduction = 50204 - 1600 = 48604

Divide by total weight = $\dfrac{48604}{2266.4}$ = **21.45** inches aft of datum.

5.4 Minimum Movement

The previous load redistribution achieved the aim, but it may not have. Even if it did, it may not have been the ideal solution. (Perhaps the load is bulky). It is better to calculate what minimum change is required to the moment, and then consider alternative methods of achieving that change in the moment.

To find the minimum moment change required, we need to calculate the difference in C of G position required, and multiply that by the total weight. For example, in the case above, the moment change required is (actual C of G position - aft limit) x 2266.4 = (22.15 - 22) x 2266.4 = 0.15 x 2266.4 = **339.96 lb in**

That moment change can often be achieved in several ways. In our example, as we have already considered, we could move baggage from the baggage compartment to the rear seat. However, we need not move all 80 lb. The minimum amount we must move can be calculated by dividing the moment change required by the change in arm (44 - 24 inches). This would give a figure of 339.96 divided by 20, or **16.998 lb**. This is the minimum mass of baggage that must be moved from the baggage compartment to the rear seat to bring the takeoff C of G position within limits.

The same moment change might be achieved in other ways, for example by changing the seating arrangements. If the passengers are different weights, for example 165 lb and 190 lb, we could move the heavy passenger from the rear seat to the front seat, and the moment change would be (heavy passenger - light passenger) x (rear arm - front arm) = 25 x 30 = 750. This is more than the minimum change required, and again would produce the desired affect, possibly in a more practical manner. Notice the care required in using the signs of the moments and arms.

5.5   Further Calculations

Even without all the original calculations, it is possible to calculate changes in loading required. For example, you may know that the total mass is 4000 kg, and that the total moment is 8000 kg m (to be totally pedantic really 80000 Nm). If the C of G limit is 1.8 m aft of datum, how much payload must be moved from hold 1 (arm 20 m) to hold 2 (arm 10 m)? The calculations would proceed thus:

Actual C of G position   = + 2 m Actual "minus" limit = 2 - 1.8 = 0.2 m

Minimum moment change   = 0.2 x mass = 800 kg m.

Minimum mass to be moved = 800 divided by arm change = 800 ÷ 10 = 80 kg

The amount of mass movement required may change from takeoff to landing. The original load sheet will show you the original takeoff and landing masses and moments. If only one requires to be altered, that will be obvious. However, if both require altering we must calculate the minimum moment change for both cases, and redistribute the load for the worst case.

1. An aircraft has an actual takeoff mass of 2400 lb, with a C of G position of 28 inches aft of datum. The maximum aft C of G limit is 27.5 inches aft. What is the minimum mass of baggage which must be moved from hold 4 (arm + 45 in) to hold 1 (arm + 18 in) to bring the C of G position within limits?

2. Using the figures in question 1, if a passenger weighing 180 lb in the rear seat (arm 31 inches aft) changes position with a passenger weighing 135 lb in the front seat (arm 4 inches forward), will the C of G return to limits?

3. An aircraft has an actual takeoff mass of 6000 lb, with a C of G position of 30 inches aft of datum. It has an actual landing mass of 5000 lb, with a C of G position of 30.5 inches aft of datum. The C of G limits are from 25 to 28 inches aft of datum. What is the minimum mass of baggage that must be moved from hold 3 (arm 40 inches aft) to hold 1 (arm 15 inches aft) to bring the C of G position within limits?

   a. 500 kg
   b. 480 kg
   c. 227 kg
   d. 218 kg

4. Using the figures in question 3, if the actual takeoff mass must be reduced by 50 lb, and it is decided to remove 50 lb of baggage, will the C of G position be within limits if that baggage is removed from hold 3?

Intentionally Left Blank

Chapter 6

Load Graphs

6.1 Introduction

Many flight manuals include graphs to make the calculation of the C of G position easier. In this chapter we shall consider two types of graph which you are likely to meet, and how they can be used to help your calculations.

6.2 The Moment Calculator

One common type of graph is represented at fig. 6.1. Instead of making mathematical calculations of moments from the mass and the arm, you simply take the mass along the **y axis** (upwards) in this case, and read off the moment along the **x axis** (along the bottom).

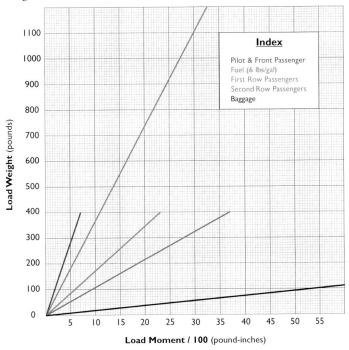

The load sheet might now take the form of fig. 6.2.

Load Sheet

MTMA: 3080 lb
MLMA: 2900 lb
C of G position limits: 42 to 52 inches aft of datum

Item	Mass (lb)	Moment (lb in)
Basic Mass	1396	20300
Pilot and Front Passenger		
First Row Passengers		
Second Row Passengers		
Baggage		
Fuel		
Total		

FIG 6.2 LOAD SHEET

If we load the aircraft as follows, we can use the graph to calculate the total moment.

Pilot		160 lb
Front Row		355 lb
Second Row		348 lb
Baggage		60 lb
Fuel	120 gals	720 lb

Load Sheet

MTMA: 3080 lb
MLMA: 2900 lb
C of G position limits: 42 to 52 inches aft of datum

Item	Mass (lb)	Moment (lb in)
Basic Mass	1396	60300
Pilot and Front Passenger	160	2800
First Row Passengers	355	20600
Second Row Passengers	348	32000
Baggage	60	32000
Fuel	720	19500
Total	3039	167200

FIG 6.3 LOAD SHEET COMPLETED

The C of G position must be calculated by dividing the moment by the mass, as usual, to give a position of **55.02** inches aft of datum.

6.3   Amending C of G Position

The previous calculation ended outside the aircraft's C of G position limits. To calculate the required load re-distribution, we must first find the required minimum moment change. The limited moment can be found by multiplying the C of G limit by the total mass;

3039 x 52 = 158028

The moment change required is 167200 - 158028 = **9172 lb in**

The effect of any redistribution can be found from the graph, in 2 stages. The first stage would be to remove the load to be re-distributed; for example a passenger weighing 174 lb from the second row would produce a moment change forward of 16000 lb in. Replacing him in the front seat, beside the pilot, would produce a moment change aft of 3000 lb in, and a total change of 13000 lb in, sufficient to produce the required change in C of G position.

Alternatively, calculate the amount of the mass change between the two positions (174 lb). Move up the **y axis** that amount, and mark the positions where that 174 lb meets the graph lines for the front passenger and for the second row. Using dividers, measure the distance between these points, and read the distance between the dividers against the **x axis** to find a moment change of **13000 lb in**.

Unfortunately, although this graphical method of calculation is quicker if the loads are inside limits, it is more complicated to calculate the necessary load re-distribution. For this reason this graph is more usually found in aircraft with wide C of G limits which are unlikely to be loaded outside these limits.

6.5   Limit Graph

The other graph a pilot is likely to meet is the graph showing the centre of gravity position limits. One of these is illustrated at fig 6.4. The pilot can transfer his mass and moment totals directly from the load sheet to the graph, and read instantly whether the C of G position is within limits.

The graph at fig 6.4 includes 2 categories; "Utility" and "Normal". Many aircraft used for training can be operated to 2 different sets of flying limitations depending on their mass and balance figures. The more restrictive figures permit flight in more extreme attitudes, for example steep turns, or practice stalling and recovery, or practice spinning and recovery (in this case - the "Utility" category). The higher figures of mass and aft C of G position only permit flight in less extreme attitudes (the 'Normal' category). The actual figures of the borders of the "Utility" category are often printed along the relevant axes of the graph, as in the case of fig 6.4.

An aeroplane in the 'Normal' category will not be allowed to carry out aerobatics or deliberate spinning, and will usually be limited to 60 degrees of bank.

As an example of how to use the limit graph, let us assume that the totals on our original load sheet turn out as a mass of 2300 lb and a moment of 32,000 lb in. We enter the graph at 2300 lb along the y axis, and at 32 along the x axis. The point giving those figures lies within the "Normal" category. Another set of results, for example a mass of 2000 lb and a moment of 26,000 lb in, gives a point inside the boundaries of the "Utility" category. It is worthy of note that this point also lies within the boundaries of the "Normal" category. In a few cases, there may be circumstances when it is advantageous to a pilot to operate his aircraft to "Normal" limits. The point plotted will actually allow flight within either "Utility" or "Normal" limits as the pilot wishes.

The shape of the limit graph is not always a parallelogram (or two in the case of different categories). Certain aircraft have differing C of G limits at different masses, and the graph will reflect that situation. Of course, the limits do not have to be shown graphically, and the written limits would reflect this.

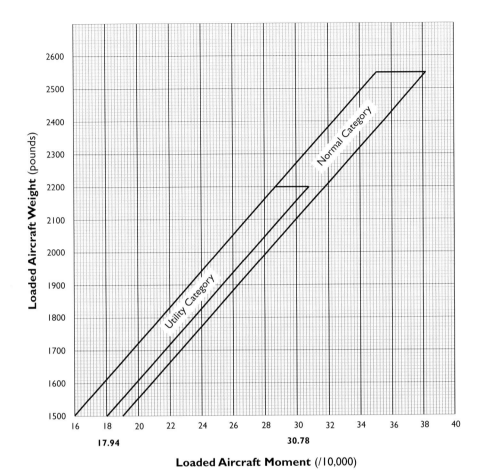

FIG 6.4 LIMIT GRAPH

6.6 Exercise

1. Using Fig 6.1 and the load sheet below, calculate the total mass and C of G position of an aircraft with a pilot weighing 180 lb, front passenger weighing 135 lb, 2 first row passengers weighing 170 lb each, and 2 second row passengers weighing 160 lb and 180 lb. 60 lb of baggage is in the baggage hold. Fuel load is 160 gallons at SG of 0.6.

Load Sheet

MTMA: 3080 lb
MLMA: 2900 lb
C of G position limits: 42 to 52 inches aft of datum

Item	Mass (lb)	Moment (lb in)
Basic Mass Pilot and Front Passenger First Row Passengers Second Row Passengers Baggage Fuel	1896	80300
Total		

2. Which change to the load distribution is the minimum to bring the takeoff C of G position back within limits?

   a. Exchanging the 160 lb passenger from the 2nd row with the passenger in the front seat
   b. Exchanging the 180 lb passenger from the 2nd row with the passenger in the front seat
   c. Neither (a) nor (b) will succeed
   d. There is no need to change the C of G position

3. Without any exchanging of loads, if the aircraft uses 120 gallons to fly to its destination, what will be the mass and C of G position on landing?

4.   Which change to the load distribution is the minimum to bring the landing C of G position back within limits?

    a.   Exchanging the 160 lb passenger from the 2nd row with the passenger in the front seat
    b.   Exchanging the 180 lb passenger from the 2nd row with the passenger in the front seat
    c.   Neither (a) nor (b) will succeed
    d.   There is no need to change the C of G position

5.   Using the graph at fig 6.4, what category may the aircraft fly in with an actual mass of 2190 lb and moment of 31,000 lb in?

6.   Using the graph at fig 6.4, what category may the aircraft fly in with a mass of 1820 lb and a moment of 23600 lb in?

7.   What flight restrictions are placed on an aeroplane in the 'normal' category?

    a.   Aerobatics are prohibited but spinning may be practised
    b.   Spinning is prohibited but aerobatics may be practised
    c.   Spinning, aerobatics and bank angles over 60 degrees are permitted
    d.   Spinning and aerobatics are prohibited, and bank angles may be restricted to 60 degrees maximum

Intentionally Left Blank

Chapter 7

Runway Definitions

7.1 Introduction

Volume 1 of this series (Air Law and Operational Procedures) includes the definitions of a runway and the declared distances. They are repeated here for ease of reference.

7.2 Runway

A runway is a **defined rectangular area prepared for the landing and taking-off of aircraft.** The surface may be hard or natural. The whole of that area is not always available for both of these functions; parts may be unusable for safe landing because of obstructions close to the end, and obstructions at the other end may limit the length available for safe take-off. There will also be unprepared or semi-prepared surfaces available at the side and either end which may be usable with varying degrees of safety in an emergency but which are not safe for regular use. All licensed aerodromes in the UK, and many others, publish the length of the completely safe usable areas as declared distances, which are described below.

   a. **LANDING**

      There is a basic **Landing Distance Available (LDA)**, which is the total length of runway less any part at the approach end which is unsafe because of obstructions or other reasons. The start of the LDA is the threshold, and if it is not also the start of the runway it is called a displaced threshold. Beyond the runway itself, there may be an area available in which an aircraft may be brought to a stop in an emergency, but which is not available for normal use, this is called the stopway. Fig 7.1 shows a runway with a displaced threshold and a stopway.

Fig 7.1 Landing Distance

b. **TAKE-OFF**

There is usually no reason why an aircraft should not start its take-off run at the beginning of the runway, and roll its wheels along the complete length and then climb away. The length declared for this is called the **Take-Off Run Available (TORA).** At the end of the TORA, there may be an area which is not suitable for an aircraft's wheels to roll on, but which is cleared of all obstructions. An aircraft taking off may **fly level** just above that area and **accelerate** to a safe climbing speed. That area is called a **clearway**, and in figure 7.2 it includes the stopway, although that is not always the case. The **TORA plus the clearway** is declared as the **Take-Off Distance Available (TODA).** If an aircraft has an emergency during its take-off roll, the pilot may decide to abandon the take-off and stop the aircraft. In that case, the stopway (if any) may be used to bring the aircraft to a halt. This total distance of **TORA plus stopway** is declared as the **Accelerate Stop Distance Available (ASDA).** Fig 7.2 shows the same runway as before but as declared for takeoff.

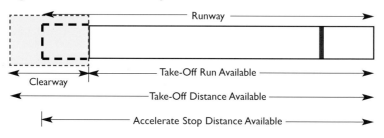

FIG 7.2 TAKEOFF DECLARATIONS

7.3   Runway Surface

The declared distances are used by pilots to decide whether they can land, take-off, or abandon a take-off safely. Other factors affect the performance of an aircraft when assessing that safety, such as slope, wind, and air density, as described later. A major factor affecting the ability of an aircraft to use its brakes efficiently, however, is the friction available between its tyres and the runway surface. Most runway surfaces give consistent braking under normal circumstances, although a grass surface will give less friction than a hard surface, and the length of the grass will affect the acceleration available on take-off. However, water on the surface will considerably affect the efficiency of brakes, and wet grass gives very little friction, especially if cut short. Ice, snow or slush will also considerably affect both take-off and landing performance, and may also affect control of the aircraft on the ground.

7.4 Runway Slope

A runway which slopes upwards will reduce the acceleration available on take-off, but will increase the deceleration after landing. Similarly, a downslope will increase take-off acceleration and reduce the braking effectiveness after landing. Runway slopes are generally measured as percentages, and can be calculated from the elevation of the two ends if necessary. For example, as in figure 7.3, a 3000 foot long runway oriented 27/09 may have a threshold elevation of 100 feet at the 27 end, and a threshold elevation of 115 feet at the 09 end. The runway slope would be (115-100 = 15) divided by 3000 = 0.5%. Runway 27 would have a 0.5% upslope, and runway 09 a 0.5% downslope. When calculating runway lengths, beware of different units. Some may be measured in metres, and one metre is 3.281 (about 3.3) feet!

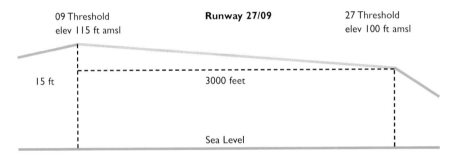

FIG. 7.3 RUNWAY SLOPE

7.5   Exercise

1. Which of the following is not one of the main declared runway distances at an aerodrome?

    a.   Take-off run available
    b.   Landing run available
    c.   Take-off distance available
    d.   Landing distance available

2. Which of the following is defined as "The length of the take-off run available plus the length of the stopway, if provided"?

    a.   Takeoff distance available
    b.   Accelerate stop distance available
    c.   Landing run available
    d.   Landing distance available

3. The length of the runway declared available and suitable for the ground run of an aircraft taking off is called:

    a.   The take-off distance available?
    b.   The accelerate-stop distance available?
    c.   The take-off run available?
    d.   The clearway?

4. The take-off run available plus the clearway is called the:

    a.   Accelerate-stop distance available?
    b.   Stopway?
    c.   Take-off distance available?
    d.   Runway?

5. A sloping runway will affect the performance of an aeroplane using it. Complete the following sentence; "A runway with an upslope will . . . . the take-off run and . . . . the landing run of an aeroplane compared with a level runway."

    a. increase. . . . . .increase
    b. increase. . . . . .decrease
    c. decrease. . . . . .increase
    d. decrease. . . . . .decrease

6. A 1000 metre runway oriented 36/18 has an elevation at the 18 threshold of 277 feet amsl. The elevation of the 36 threshold is 293 feet amsl. What is the slope on runway 18?

    a. 1.5% up
    b. 0.5% up
    c. 1.5% down
    d. 0.5% down

Intentionally Left Blank

Chapter 8

Take-Off Performance

8.1 Introduction

As seen in chapter 1, an aeroplane during take-off requires to produce enough lift to overcome its weight, and a little more to start climbing. The heavier the aircraft, the more lift will be required to balance that weight. We should now look at the way in which that lift is produced, and then at the factors affecting the amount of runway required to accelerate sufficiently to achieve that lift. The runway required to reach a point at which the aeroplane can lift off the runway can be called the "take-off run required" (TORR). However, in most cases, the pilot is interested in the distance needed to reach a safe height above the runway, often considered to be 50 feet. The distance from the start of the take-off run to the point at which the aeroplane has reached that safe height is the "take-off distance required" or TODR, as marked in figures 8.3 to 8.7. An aeroplane can be expected to make a safe take-off if the take-off run available is greater than the take-off run required, and the take-off distance available is greater than the take-off distance required.

8.2 Aerodynamic Forces

An aeroplane moving forward deflects the air through which it is passing by its shape. Mathematicians quote Newton's third law to say that 'to every action there is an equal and opposite reaction', which suggests that this deflection of the air produces a force which tries to move the aeroplane itself. This 'total reaction' force attempts to push the aeroplane backwards and upwards. We normally think of the part of that total reaction which is acting directly backwards from the direction of movement as 'drag', and the component which is acting at right angles to that (upwards in an aeroplane flying level) we call 'lift'. These 'aerodynamic' forces of lift and drag depend on the amount (the mass) of air deflected and the angle of deflection.

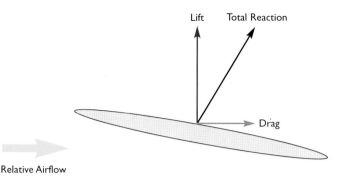

FIG 8.1 AERODYNAMIC FORCES

The wing is the part of the aeroplane designed to produce most of the lift force. It deflects the air downwards from the direction of flight. The amount of air deflected (its mass) determines the amount of aerodynamic force produced. The angle through which the air is deflected decides the proportion of the aerodynamic force which is lift and which proportion is drag.

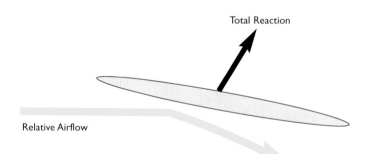

FIG 8.2 AIRFLOW DEFLECTION

The size of the wing (the 'wing area') affects the mass of air deflected. The shape of the wing, and indeed of the whole aircraft, determines the angle of deflection, and also affects the mass deflected. The angle at which the air meets the shape effectively changes the shape presented to the air, so that 'angle of attack' is also of prime importance in determining the mass of air deflected and the angle of deflection, hence the drag and lift produced. However, the air itself contributes to the forces. The greater the air's mass per unit of volume, its 'density', the more force will be produced, and the faster the air is moving relative to the wing (the true airspeed or TAS) the more air will be deflected in a given period of time.

These factors are traditionally included in the lift formula $L = C_L \frac{1}{2} \rho V^2 S$. S is the wing area, V is the TAS, and ρ is the density of the air. C_L, the 'coefficient of lift', takes account of the shape of the wing and the angle of attack. The combination of speed and air density ($\frac{1}{2}\rho V^2$) is referred to as the 'dynamic pressure' of the air against the aircraft. Although the airspeed indicator to which the pilot refers in flight is actually measuring that dynamic pressure, and the **indicated** airspeed at which the aircraft takes off will remain constant for a given weight, we need to consider all the factors individually when thinking about aeroplane performance.

8.3   Air Density

Air density is a factor in providing aerodynamic force. It is also a major factor in providing thrust from an engine. Aircraft engines burn fuel in air to produce heat energy, which in a piston engine is converted into mechanical energy turning a crankshaft and propeller. The more dense the air entering the engine, the more fuel can be burnt in that air and the more energy produced.

The mechanical energy transmitted to the propeller has to be turned into a thrust force to overcome the aircraft's drag and accelerate it to a TAS sufficient for the wings to generate enough lift to take-off. A propeller converts its turning motion into aerodynamic force by its own shape, rotation speed, blade angle and forward speed (the combination of which last two affecting the angle of attack), so the thrust from the propeller also depends on the air density.

Air density has a considerable effect on the length of runway required for an aeroplane to take off. Not only does it affect the lift available from the wings, it also affects the acceleration of the aircraft from rest to the airspeed required to climb. The density of the air itself depends on its temperature and pressure, increasing as temperature decreases, and decreasing as pressure decreases (as altitude increases). A temperature increase of 10 degrees Celsius, or an increase in airfield elevation of 1000 feet, can each produce a 10% increase in take-off distance. The weight, altitude and temperature (WAT) limits mentioned in Chapter 1 take account of the density factor in climb performance after take-off.

Density is also affected to a certain extent by the humidity of the air (moist air is less dense than dry air), although humidity will usually have a greater effect on engine performance than on the lift from the wings. Most aircraft manufacturers ignore the effect of humidity, although a few companies include factors in their Flight Manuals.

In order to take account of air density in performance calculations, the actual air density sometimes has to be converted to a 'density altitude'. This is the pressure altitude (altitude in the International Standard Atmosphere) at which the density would be the same as the actual conditions experienced at the aerodrome surface The navigation computer can be used to calculate this from actual pressure altitude and air temperature, or there may be a table in the Flight Manual. The greater the density altitude, the longer the take-off distance.

8.4   True Air Speed

To achieve a particular air speed, the aircraft must accelerate along the runway. If air density is low, that true air speed will need to be higher than in conditions of high air density.   We have already seen that the rate of acceleration will be less in these conditions of low air density, so the effect is compounded. Calculations for density include the TAS effect.

8.5   Runway Surface

For rapid acceleration, the aircraft wheels must rotate freely. Unlubricated bearings and incorrect tyre pressures will increase the drag of the wheels, as will mud packed into wheel spats. However, the actual surface of the runway has a considerable effect. A hard, dry runway allows rapid acceleration to take-off speeds, but a soft surface (or snow) may allow the wheels to sink into the ground and reduce the rate of acceleration. Grass will drag at the wheels; the longer the grass the more drag will be produced, and wet grass has a greater effect than dry grass. The increase in runway required if taking off on wet grass is shown in figure 8.3. Standing water on a hard runway will not only produce drag at the wheels, but may also cause aquaplaning (skidding) and the loss of directional control, so must be avoided.

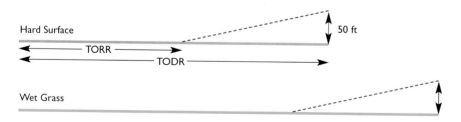

FIG 8.3 EFFECT ON TAKE-OFF PERFORMANCE OF A WET GRASS RUNWAY

8.6 Runway Slope

We have looked at how to calculate the slope of a runway in Chapter 7. If the runway slopes upwards, the aeroplane engine(s) have to push it uphill while attempting to accelerate. It therefore takes a longer time and a longer distance to achieve the correct speed for lift off. Conversely, a downhill slope will allow the aeroplane to accelerate quicker, but to a lesser extent. An uphill slope of 2% (approximately 30 feet over a 450 metre runway) will increase the take-off distance by up to 10%, as shown in figure 8.4.

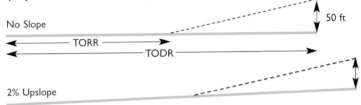

FIGURE 8.4 EFFECT OF UPSLOPE ON TAKE-OFF

It is important to note the greater effect which runway slope and surface have on the ground run (TORR) compared with the take-off distance to 50 feet. Although perhaps of only minor importance for examination purposes, this should be borne in mind when making practical calculations.

8.7 Wind

Because the aeroplane requires a certain airspeed to achieve the necessary lift, any head or tail wind will affect the time and distance required to reach that airspeed. A headwind means that the aeroplane has already reached a certain airspeed while standing still; a tailwind means that it must accelerate to that groundspeed before it has any airspeed at all! A tailwind will have a proportionately greater effect on take-off or landing performance than a headwind. A tailwind component of 10% of the take-off speed (5 knots if the aeroplane takes off at a typical 50 knots) will increase the take-off distance required by up to 20%, as shown in figure 8.5.

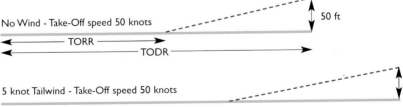

FIGURE 8.5 EFFECT OF 5 KNOT TAILWIND ON TYPICAL LIGHT AEROPLANE

The amount of head or tail wind component must be calculated, but to allow for the unpredictability of the wind at any time, only half of the forecast headwind should be used, and any expected tailwind should be assumed to be one and a half times its forecast strength.

A wind directly across the runway will give no head or tail wind component, but will reduce performance to some extent because control deflections to keep straight and level on the runway increase drag and reduce acceleration.

8.8 Configuration

Many aeroplanes have flap settings which are marked as "take-off" (typically flap lowered by 10∞). Some offer a choice of various amounts of flap which a pilot might consider using during the take-off. All flap settings change the shape of the wing, and therefore the amount of lift available. More lift is available at a given (low) airspeed, or the same lift can be achieved at a lower airspeed. However, the change of shape also increases the drag from the wing, proportionately more at higher speeds, so acceleration is reduced. Rate of climb is also reduced, so if flaps are used during the take-off, the aeroplane will probably use less runway to reach lift-off speed (a reduced TORR), but take a greater overall distance to climb to 50 feet (a greater TODR), as shown in figure 8.6. In any case, the techniques and flap settings advised in the Flight Manual (see below) should be followed for best performance.

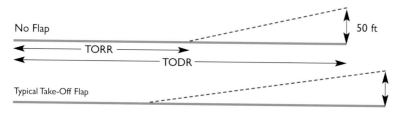

FIG 8.6 TYPICAL EFFECT OF TAKE-OFF FLAP

When taking off on soft ground, the shorter run with flaps is usually beneficial. If there are obstacles under the initial climb path, however, manufacturers usually recommend taking off with the flaps retracted. Although the ideal maximum obstacle clearance may be obtained by selecting take-off flap for lift-off and retracting it once airborne, the dangers of losing lift at low speed (and perhaps stalling) during flap retraction close to the ground means that this technique is not recommended.

8.9 Wing Condition

Anything which affects the surface of the wing will detract from its efficiency, and therefore the lift produced. Dirt, insects, water drops or ice will all affect it, but the degree to which any surface irregularities affect a particular aeroplane depend on the wing's individual characteristics, and the Flight Manual should be consulted for advice. For example, raindrops on the wings of a touring motor glider may reduce the lift available considerably, and therefore increase the take-off distance required.

Any ice, or even frost, on the wing of any aeroplane will reduce the performance; often to such an extent that take-off might be impossible. The extra weight of any such ice will add to the problems as shown below (although to a much lesser extent than the aerodynamic effects), so for both these reasons any ice must be removed completely before flight.

8.10 Weight

The aircraft's weight influences several factors in take-off performance, which combine to affect the take-off distance and take-off run (ground run) required.

- A greater weight requires more lift to raise it off the runway, and therefore the airspeed required to produce that lift, so the aircraft must stay on the ground longer while accelerating.
- A greater weight produces more friction on the runway surface, therefore more drag, which reduces the acceleration, so the distance required to reach even the original airspeed would be increased.
- A greater weight reduces the rate of climb after leaving the runway.

It has been calculated that a 10% increase in weight (for example a second 165 pound pilot in a Cessna 152) produces approximately:

- a 5% increase in take-off airspeed required
- a 9% decrease in acceleration, and
- a 20% increase in take off distance required, as represented in figure 8.7

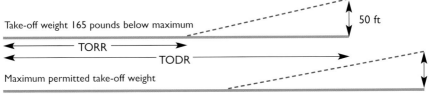

FIG 8.7 EFFECT OF WEIGHT ON CESSNA 152 TAKE-OFF PERFORMANCE

8.11 The Flight Manual

Handbooks for aircraft are sometimes referred to as the 'pilot's operating handbook' or similar, but the official Flight Manual is produced by the manufacturer and is part of the Certificate of Airworthiness of the aircraft, approved by the state of manufacture. It must also be approved by the state of registry. The CAA provides the approval for UK registered aircraft, although increasingly the JAA is taking on responsibility for aircraft certification, and approval from any JAA state's authority on behalf of the JAA has equivalent validity. However, the state of registry may require changes or additions to the flight manual to comply with their own regulations. These are published in the form of "supplements", and are often related to the published performance figures. Pilots must ensure that they use the approved figures where these differ from those in the original document.

The Flight Manual, and any handbooks which contain extracts from it, are traditionally divided into standard sections. Section 1 is usually general information, section 2 contains the aircraft limitations, section 3 contains emergency procedures, section 4 normal operating procedures, section 5 performance data, section 6 weight and balance information, and section 7 includes description of the aircraft systems.

In section 5, the manufacturer provides information about take-off performance. This will usually be the take-off run required and/or the take-off distance required. However these figures are normally ideal ones for particular conditions of temperature and pressure (ISA or standard conditions of +15°C at 1013 hPa) on a flat, hard, dry runway, and require the pilot to use the techniques given in the Flight Manual without error. Any changes to the standard conditions or techniques will change the distances required.

In some manuals, there are tables or lists of factors which should be applied to take account of some or all of the conditions listed above. However, in their absence, the factors described below in paragraph 8.14, and listed in the CAA's Aeronautical Information Circular (AIC) and Safety Sense Leaflet (no.7) on aeroplane performance, must be applied.

In other manuals, there are graphs to take account of many of the factors to be applied, as described in chapter 10. However, some at least of the factors may be omitted from the graph, and have to be applied separately

8.12 Net Performance

The information given in the Flight Manual is obtained by a test pilot flying a new aircraft, following the recommended procedures exactly. As aircraft grow older, engine performance deteriorates, and drag increases because of skin friction from an airframe surface which has almost certainly also deteriorated. In addition, the average pilot cannot be expected to fly as accurately as a test pilot. Aeroplanes operated for the purposes of public transport must add an extra allowance to take-off (and landing) calculations to take account of these considerations. Some Flight Manuals may include these allowances, but unless that is specifically stated, pilots are strongly advised to also add that allowance themselves. For take-off, the allowance depends on the accelerate/stop distance available (ASDA). For simplicity, the CAA suggests that an additional factor of 1.33 should be applied to take-off calculations to give a similar additional safety factor.

8.13 Take-off Technique

The techniques used by the test pilot to produce the performance figures in the flight manual are normally written in that manual. Any other technique, for example raising the nosewheel at a different speed, or using a different flap setting, will increase the runway length required. It is worth noting that sometimes the recommended technique is difficult to follow, and may be contrary to that for which the pilot's previous training has prepared him. In such a case, even the allowance mentioned in paragraph 8.12 may not ensure safety. Pilots should check the Flight Manual figures themselves on a long runway before relying on them on a short one.

8.14 Calculation Factors

The factors to take account of the conditions in the sections above must be applied one by one. If the approved Flight Manual includes allowances for the conditions, these should be applied. Each consideration will have an effect on the distances required, so all the factors must be **multiplied together** to determine their total effect. If there are no allowances in the approved flight manual for any or all of these conditions, the factors listed below, published by the CAA in an Aeronautical Information Circular (AIC), must be used to multiply the ideal figure in the Flight Manual to calculate the final take-off distance required. However, the listed factors must only be used in adverse situations; any conditions which might reduce the take-off distance (for example a downslope) must be ignored in calculations unless specifically included in the Flight Manual.

As mentioned in paragraph 8.6 above, the effect of surface or slope on the ground roll will be greater than that on the overall take-off distance.

Condition	Increase in TODR	Factor
A 10% increase in aircraft weight from that quoted in the Flight Manual	20%	1.2
An increase of 1000 feet in aerodrome elevation	10%	1.1
An increase of 10° C in ambient temperature	10%	1.1
A 2% slope uphill	10%	1.1
A tailwind component of 10% of the lift-off speed	20%	1.2
Surface of dry grass, up to 20 cm (8") long	20%	1.2
Surface of wet grass, up to 20 cm (8") long	30%	1.3
Surface of soft ground or snow	25% or more	1.25
Additional factor if Flight Manual figures are gross (unfactored)		1.33

1. For an aeroplane to make a safe take-off, which of the following conditions are necessary?

   a. TORA must not be less than TODA and TORR must not be less than TODR
   b. TODR must not be less than TODA and TORR must not be less than TORA
   c. TODA must not be less than TODR and TORA must not be less than TORR
   d. TODA must not be less than TORA and TODR must not be less than TORR

2. Which of the following is correct?

   a. An increase in temperature causes an increase in air density and an increase in take-off run required.
   b. An increase in temperature causes an increase in air density and a decrease in take-off run required
   c. An increase in temperature causes a decrease in air density and an increase in take-off run required
   d. An increase in temperature causes a decrease in air density and a decrease in take-off run required

3. The surface wind is forecast 240/20 knots. The runway direction is 240°. What wind should the pilot use for his take-off calculations?

   a. 10 knots headwind
   b. 30 knots headwind
   c. 10 knots tailwind
   d. 30 knots tailwind

4. Which of the following will not increase take-off distance available by 20%?

   a. A tailwind of 10% of the take-off speed
   b. An increase of 1000 feet in aerodrome elevation
   c. A 10% increase in weight
   d. A dry grass runway

5. What safety factor should be applied if flight manual take-off performance figures are unfactored?

   a. 1.10
   b. 1.20
   c. 1.25
   d. 1.33

6. The runway surface is short wet grass. What factor should be applied to the published take-off distance required to take this into account?

    a. 1.20
    b. 1.25
    c. 1.30
    d. 1.33

7. What effect will the use of take-off flap have on take-off performance?

    a. Take-off run and take-off distance will both increase
    b. Take-off run and take-off distance will both reduce
    c. Take-off run will increase but take-off distance will decrease
    d. Take-off run will decrease but take-off distance will increase

8. Which of the following conditions produces a different factor in take-off performance calculations from the others?

    a. A decrease in airfield altitude of 1000 feet
    b. An increase in ambient temperature of 10°C
    c. A 2° uphill slope
    d. A 5% increase in aircraft weight

Chapter 9

Landing Performance

9.1   Introduction

As with a take-off, an aeroplane must be able to land on whatever runway is available to it. For that reason, landing performance calculations must be made carefully. Many of the factors affecting take-off have similar effects on the landing ground run required, and more importantly the distance required from a 'screen height' of 50 feet (or 15 metres), but to differing degrees. This chapter attempts to explain these factors.

9.2   Technique

The published figures assume that the landing aeroplane reaches the screen height above the runway threshold on the approach at the recommended indicated airspeed and configuration, and continues its landing using the recommended technique in the Flight Manual. This normally involves closing the throttle at the same time as changing the attitude to land on the main wheels for an aeroplane with a tricycle undercarriage, or on all three wheels for one with a tailwheel. The energy of a landing aeroplane, which must be reduced by a combination of drag and the aircraft's brakes, is the product of its mass and the square of its speed. If the pilot reaches the screen height at a higher speed than recommended, the landing distance required is considerably greater than that which his calculations would indicate. A 10% increase in threshold speed produces a 20% increase in landing distance.

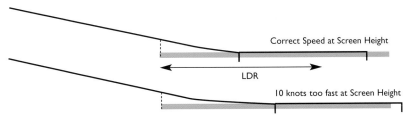

FIG 9.1 EFFECT OF THRESHOLD SPEED ON LANDING DISTANCE

9.3 Airspeed

The speed at which an aeroplane should cross the runway threshold (at screen height) is a compromise between two conflicting requirements. On one hand, it is important that the aircraft has a safe margin of control, and will not stall if it encounters a gust. On the other hand, if the aircraft is flying too fast, it will require a very long runway to stop, and the pilot may find a tendency to over-control on the round-out.

The accepted method of calculating the correct threshold speed (sometimes called reference speed or V_{REF}) is to apply a factor of 1.3 to the stalling speed in the landing configuration and weight (mathematically, $V_{REF} = 1.3\ V_S$). However, most Flight Manuals publish recommended speeds for different conditions, and these should be used at the appropriate time.

Note that manufacturers often publish landing distances required which are calculated using so-called "short field" techniques, which involve a lower threshold speed than that recommended for normal operations. Short landing techniques require considerable practice, and involve approaching at a slower indicated airspeed, with a higher than usual angle of attack and more power to counter the resulting drag. That increased power produces a decrease in stalling speed which allows a reduced V_{REF} if the technique is properly applied, but there is less margin for error in the round-out.

There are some other conditions which may change the speed at which the pilot makes his approach. Let us consider an approach without power (a glide approach). A windmilling propeller creates drag even before the round-out, but that implies that the approach path itself will be steeper than normal, and the aircraft attitude on that approach will also be steeper. The change in attitude needed at the round-out will be greater than usual, so although the increase in stalling speed without power is normally taken into account when calculating the normal threshold speed, manufacturers normally recommend increasing approach and threshold speeds by about 5 knots if making an approach without power. This increases the landing run and distance required.

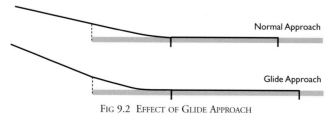

FIG 9.2 EFFECT OF GLIDE APPROACH

9.4   Use of flaps

Flaps are used during an approach for two reasons. The extra drag, especially in the full, or landing, flap configuration allows the pilot to make a steep approach to clear obstacles under the approach path. Because flaps decrease an aeroplane's stalling speed, their use allows for a lower threshold speed. This has the result that any approach without the use of flap in an aeroplane which is designed to use them must be flown faster than normal. Usually manufacturers recommend an increase of 5 knots in both the initial approach speed and the threshold speed. The reduced drag without flap on the approach can make accurate speed control difficult, and increases the landing distance required, as does the increased speed.

Full flap is normally recommended for landing. The difference in lift produced, and therefore stalling speed, between full flap and half flap (or "take-off" flap) is usually regarded as insignificant, although differences in airflow around the static vents may affect the **indicated** airspeed. In any case, as the amount of flap deflection increases, so does the amount of drag produced. To minimise the landing distance required, full flap should be used, and in most published figures that is assumed. Nevertheless, many aeroplanes are easier to control in crosswinds with less than full flap. If using such a crosswind landing technique, pilots must be aware that the landing distance required will be greater than that published. Some Flight Manuals may include graphs for calculating landing distance required for different flap settings.

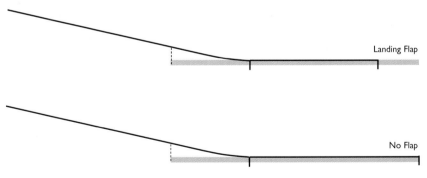

Fig 9.3 Effect of flap on landing distance

9.5 Air Density

As we saw in the last chapter, the density of the air has an effect on the true air speed of an aircraft when compared with the indicated airspeed. The recommended indicated airspeed for passing the screen height (the 'reference speed') is related to the stalling speed in that particular configuration. If the air density is lower than that in the standard atmosphere at sea level (3225 gm/cm³), the true air speed will be greater than the indication, as will the resultant groundspeed. A high groundspeed means that the aircraft needs a longer ground run to slow down, and more energy must be absorbed by the brakes.

In addition, the lower density reduces the drag from the airframe, requiring the brakes to work harder to slow the aeroplane. An aircraft engine has less power in that lower density, which one might suggest would produce less thrust to counter the airframe drag, but in a propeller driven aeroplane the windmilling propeller produces drag, not thrust. An increase in airfield elevation of 1000 feet increases the landing distance required by 5%.

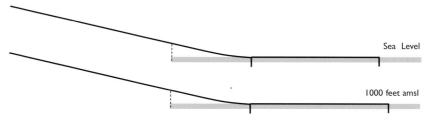

FIG 9.4 EFFECT OF ALTITUDE ON LANDING DISTANCE

9.6 Temperature

An increase in temperature produces a reduction in density, and also reduces the effectiveness of brakes, which can be particularly important in large aeroplanes. However, in a light aircraft, a 10°C increase in ambient temperature should be regarded as producing a 5% increase in the landing distance required.

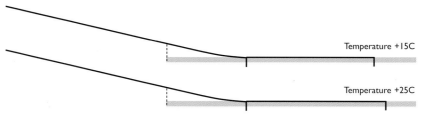

FIG 9.5 EFFECT OF TEMPERATURE ON LANDING DISTANCE

64

9.7   Weight

At a higher weight, stalling speed increases, so the speed recommended at screen height is also higher, as is the speed at which the aircraft touches down. The energy of a landing aircraft, which must be absorbed by airframe drag and the brakes, is a product of its mass and the square of its groundspeed.   Both these factors are affected by an increase in landing weight, so an increase in landing weight of 10% (as our earlier example of a second pilot in a Cessna 152) increases the landing distance required by an equivalent 10%.

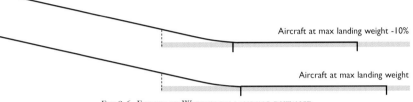

Aircraft at max landing weight -10%

Aircraft at max landing weight

FIG 9.6   EFFECT OF WEIGHT ON LANDING DISTANCE

9.8   Wind

Readers may have noticed that weight, altitude and temperature have approximately half the effect on landing as they do on take-off. These might be considered the factors affecting the aeroplane itself. However, the factors affecting the runway itself cannot be quite so simply remembered, although the wind has a generally similar effect on landing distance to the effect on take-off distance seen in the last chapter.

A tailwind will have a similar effect on the landing distance required as it has on the take-off distance, and for similar reasons. The distance from screen height to touchdown will be greater, and the groundspeed on touchdown will be greater, increasing the energy which must be dissipated by drag and the brakes. A tailwind of 10% of the touchdown speed (which can be considered as virtually the same as the lift-off speed for the same weight) will produce an increase in landing distance required of 20%.

As with take-off calculations, any forecast wind head or tail component must itself be factorised. Pilots should use only 50% of a forecast headwind component, and 150% of a forecast tailwind component.

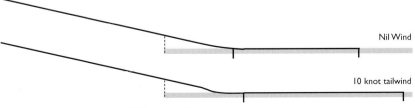

Nil Wind

10 knot tailwind

FIG 9.7   EFFECT OF TAILWIND ON LANDING DISTANCE

9.9   Runway Surface

Certain aeroplanes with no brakes may find that their landing distance is actually reduced on dry grass, because of the drag on the wheels. However, for most aeroplanes fitted with brakes, the reduction in braking effect available will more than counter that drag. A runway covered with fairly short (less than 8 inches long) dry grass will increase the landing distance required by 15%. Brakes are effectively lubricated by water from a wet surface, and lose some of their effect, which coupled with the slipping felt by the tyres against the surface will cause an increase in the landing run and therefore overall distance required. A wet paved surface will require about a 15% increase in landing distance required, similar to that on dry grass. On wet grass, where the tyres can be expected to slip more, the increase will be about 35% on firm soil. Soft ground will produce an increase of about 25% or more, as will snow.

A particular problem may occur if the landing is made on wet and very short grass (but firm underfoot). This surface can be very slippery, providing little retardation from the brakes and a risk of losing directional control during the landing run. On such a surface, pilots should assume they will require a very long landing distance - up to 60% more than on a dry paved surface.

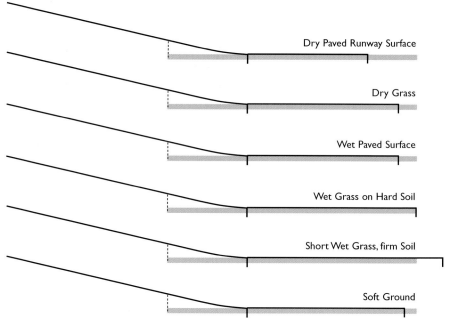

Dry Paved Runway Surface

Dry Grass

Wet Paved Surface

Wet Grass on Hard Soil

Short Wet Grass, firm Soil

Soft Ground

FIG 9.8 EFFECT OF RUNWAY SURFACE ON LANDING DISTANCE

9.10 Slope

Runway slope affects the landing as much as the take-off. However, in this case an upslope will allow the weight of the aeroplane to assist in slowing it down. If the runway slopes downwards, that weight will act against the drag and the brakes, and a longer distance will be required to stop. A 2% downhill slope will produce an increase in the required landing distance of 10%, nearly all accounted for by the landing run after touchdown.

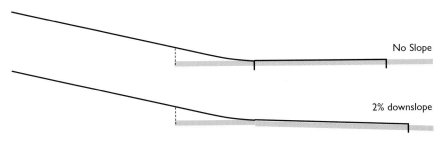

FIG 9.9 EFFECT OF RUNWAY SLOPE ON LANDING DISTANCE

9.11 Net Performance

As with take-off calculations, regulations require that aeroplanes used for public transport apply a safety factor. In the case of landing performance, that factor is 1.43. Again, it is recommended that private pilots apply the same factor. However, pilots should remember that this safety factor is intended to take account of the inaccuracies which might be expected in public transport aircraft flown by commercial pilots. It is not designed to compensate for major errors.

9.12 Calculation Factors for Landing Performance

Again, the factors we have looked at each have an effect on the landing distance required, and in the case of surface and slope a greater effect on the landing ground run. If the flight manual approved by the JAA (or CAA) contains factors for any of the circumstances mentioned, they should be applied. Otherwise the factors in the table below, contained in the CAA's Aeronautical Information Circular (AIC) on light aeroplane performance, should be used, with regard to any special advice in the previous paragraphs. If more than one adverse circumstance is present (for example tailwind and grass surface), the factors must be multiplied together, as in the case of take-off calculations.

The factors in the table must not, however, be applied in reverse. A headwind of 5 knots, for example, provides less reduction in landing distance than the increase caused by a 5 knot tailwind. Unless they are specifically mentioned with their own factors in the flight manual, favourable effects must not be included in calculations, but should be regarded as a bonus.

If, after applying all the factors to the published landing distance required, the calculated LDR is less than the landing distance available as published or measured, the landing can safely be made provided the correct techniques are used. However, remember you may wish to take-off again, and taking off normally needs more runway than landing, so it is usually advisable to make the take-off calculations before you land!

Condition	Increase in LDR	Factor
A 10% increase in aircraft weight from that quoted in the Flight Manual	10%	1.1
An increase of 1000 feet in aerodrome elevation	5%	1.05
An increase of 10° C in ambient temperature	5%	1.05
A 2% slope downhill	10%	1.1
A tailwind component of 10% of the lift-off speed	20%	1.2
Surface of dry grass, up to 20 cm (8") long	15%	1.15
Wet paved surface	15%	1.15
Surface of wet grass, up to 20 cm (8") long, but see below for short wet grass	35%	1.35
Surface of short wet grass on firm soil	up to 60% or more	1.6?
Surface of soft ground or snow	25% or more	1.25
Additional factor if Flight Manual figures are gross (unfactored)		1.43

1.   If the stalling speed of an aeroplane in the approach configuration is 40 knots, what would be the correct speed at the threshold?

     a.   40 knots
     b.   52 knots
     c.   57 knots
     d.   63 knots

2.   Compared with an approach with full flap, what would be the effect of a landing without flap?

     a.   Recommended threshold speed and landing distance are both reduced
     b.   Recommended threshold speed is reduced, landing distance is increased
     c.   Recommended threshold speed is increased, landing distance is reduced
     d.   Recommended threshold speed and landing distance are both increased

3.   Which of the following will produce the greatest increase in landing distance?

     a.   An increase in airfield elevation of 1700 feet
     b.   A 2% upslope
     c.   A 15 degree increase in air temperature
     d.   A 6% increase in aircraft weight

4.   Which of the following runway surfaces is likely to produce the longest landing distance?

     a.   Dry concrete
     b.   Dry short grass
     c.   Wet short grass, soft underfoot
     d.   Wet short grass, firm underfoot

5.   What increase in landing distance should be expected if the runway surface is short dry grass?

     a.   5%
     b.   10%
     c.   15%
     d.   20%

6. What increase in landing distance should be expected if the runway surface is very short wet grass?

    a. 10%
    b. 20%
    c. 30%
    d. 60%

7. Use of a higher approach speed than recommended in the flight manual will:

    a. Increase the landing roll and also the total landing distance required
    b. Have no effect on the landing roll but increase the total landing distance required
    c. Increase the landing roll but have no effect on the total landing distance required
    d. Have no effect on either the landing roll or the total landing distance required

8. Which of the following is not an effect of using flap on the approach?

    a. Stalling speed is reduced
    b. Threshold speed is reduced
    c. The approach angle can be steeper
    d All the above are true

9. A runway is measured as having an average slope of 1% downwards over its whole length. What effect does the AIC suggest this will have on the landing distance required, compared with a runway with no slope?

    a. The landing distance required will be increased by 2%
    b. The landing distance required will increase by 5%
    c. The landing distance required will increase by 10%
    d. The landing distance required will increase by 20%

Chapter 10

Runway Calculations

10.1 Introduction

We have looked at the theory of take-off and landing calculations, which are the basis of many examination questions. However, as mentioned in the previous chapters, many Flight Manuals contain tables or graphs which include some, if not all, of the factors required for the relevant performance calculations. In this chapter we shall describe some of the calculations which you will be required to make for practical purposes using typical Flight Manual information. These are the calculations which a flight examiner will expect you to make during the pre-flight preparation part of your skills test.

10.2 Tables

Tables may be in the form of the one below, which is an extract from one found in the Flight Manual of a Cessna 152.

TAKE OFF DISTANCE
SHORT FIELD

CONDITIONS:

Flaps 10°, Full Throttle Prior to Brake Release, Paved, Dry Runway, Zero Wind.

NOTES:

1. Short Field Technique as specified in Section 4 of the Flight Manual
2. Prior to take-off from fields above 3000 feet elevation, the mixture should be leaned to give maximum RPM at full throttle, static runup.
3. Decrease distances 10% for each 9 knots headwind. For operation with tailwinds up to 10 knots, increase distance by 10% for each 2 knots.
4. For operation on a dry, grass runway, increase distances by 15% of the "ground roll" figures

Weight lbs	Takeoff Speed KIAS		Press Alt Feet	0°C		10°C		20°C		30°C		40°C	
	Lift Off	50 ft		Grnd Roll	Total to clear 50 ft obst	Grnd Roll	Total to clear 50 ft obst	Grnd Roll	Total to clear 50 ft obst	Grnd Roll	Total to clear 50 ft obst	Grnd Roll	Total to clear 50 ft obst
1670	50	54	SL	640	1190	695	1290	755	1390	810	1495	875	1605
			1000	705	1310	765	1420	825	1530	890	1645	960	1770
			2000	775	1445	840	1565	910	1690	980	1820	1055	1960
			3000	855	1600	925	1730	1000	1870	1080	2020	1165	2185
			4000	940	1775	1020	1920	1100	2080	1190	2250	1285	2440
			5000	1040	1970	1125	2140	1215	2320	1315	2525	1420	2750

The basic use of the table is simple. However, as mentioned in the previous chapters, this table is only valid when the pilot uses the techniques recommended in the Flight Manual, section 4. The pilot must first check that the Certificate of Airworthiness allows the use of these techniques, and of this table. He should then ensure that he has practised the techniques before using them when performance is marginal.

To calculate the takeoff distance required in this aircraft on any particular occasion, the pilot must know what conditions apply. If the aircraft is at a weight of 1670 lb, the runway is level with a hard surface, and there is no wind, the aerodrome is at sea level, and the air pressure at the aerodrome is 1013 hectopascals (or millibars - the same thing), the pilot can read the required distances direct from the top line of the table against the surface temperature. For example, with the temperature of 20°C, the take-off run required will be 755 feet, and the take-off distance required (to clear a 50 foot obstruction) is 1390 feet. However, as we saw in chapter 8, if the figures are "gross" (have not been factorised for public transport use), for safety we need to multiply these figures by 1.33, giving a TORR of 1004 feet and a TODR of 1849 feet.

If the temperature is not one of the figures specified in the table, it may seem logical to interpolate, as described in chapter 11, paragraph 11.5. For example, at 15°C, the TORR before applying the 1.33 factor should be halfway between 695 and 755. However, most Flight Manuals recommend rounding up to the higher figure always, which in this case would be 755 as before.

A problem posed by this table is to decide the aerodrome pressure altitude. This is the altitude shown on the aircraft's altimeter when the aircraft is on the runway with the altimeter subscale set to 1013 hPa. It may be found from certain navigation computers, or from graphs in the Flight Manual, or by remembering that a pressure change of 1 hPa equates to approximately 30 feet in pressure altitude at sea level (a decrease in pressure - QNH less than 1013 - equates to an increase in pressure altitude and vice versa). However, the practical method is to set the altimeter sub-scale to 1013 and read the indicated altitude from the instrument. Again, most Flight Manuals recommend rounding up to the next quoted altitude, so if the pressure altitude is between 0 and 1000 feet, use the row corresponding to 1000 feet. In our example, if the pressure drops and the pressure altitude becomes 100 feet, the TORR becomes 825 feet before multiplying by the safety factor of 1.33, giving 1097 feet. The TODR would be 1530 x 1.33 = 2035 feet.

Let us now consider the wind. The table gives factors for the wind, but we must remember to use only 50% of a reported headwind, and 150% of a reported tailwind. If the headwind component were 8 knots, we must only use 4 knots for the performance calculations. The table gives a factor for each 9 knots, but again it is advisable not to interpolate, but to use still air in this case. If there were a tailwind component, let us say 2 knots, we must take 150% of that, giving 3 knots. In this case, it is practical to multiply the distances by 15%, which in our example would give a TORR of 1097 x 1.15 = 1262 feet and a TODR of 2035 x 1.15 = 2340 feet.

If the runway surface in our example were dry grass, the table suggests that the figures should have a distance of 15% of the ground roll added, which in this case is 124 feet. However, that must be added BEFORE any other factorisation takes place, in other words right at the beginning. To calculate take-off figures for our example from a dry grass runway with the previously calculated tailwind the calculations become, for TORR (825 + 124 =) 949 x 1.33 x 1.15 = 1452, and for TODR (1530 + 124 =) 1654 x 1.33 x 1.15 = 2530 feet. However, the table gives no factors for wet grass, so if the grass were wet the factors listed in the table in chapter 8 would have to be used, and our figure for TODR in our example would then become 1530 x 1.33 x 1.15 x 1.3 = 3042 feet. Accurate figures for take-off run required are difficult to calculate in such circumstances.

The table gives no corrections for runway slope. For that we must again refer to the CAA factors given in chapter 8, multiplying by the requisite factor. If our example runway sloped down by 1%, that should theoretically reduce our TORR and TODR, but for calculations we must ignore the downslope.

The table also makes no allowance for any reduced all up weight at take-off, so we must assume that the figures apply at all permitted weights.

10.3 Comparison

Once we have calculated our take-off run required and take-off distance required, we must compare them with the published runway length and take-off distance available. These can be obtained from the aerodrome, but are routinely published in the Aeronautical Information Publication (AIP) for licensed aerodromes. Commercially available VFR guides such as Pooley's provide data for most aerodromes, licensed or not, in the UK. Let us assume that the grass runway is dry, with a length (TORA) of 450 metres, and a TODA of 700 metres. We have calculated our TORR is 1452 feet. 450 metres is 1476 feet, so the aircraft should be able to lift off the runway before the end. 700 metres is 2297 feet. The take-off cannot be safely made, because we cannot be sure the aircraft will clear the obstruction which limits the take-off distance (TODR is 3042 feet).

Our example assumed a light tailwind component. Practically, it would be possible to make the take-off in a suitable headwind, so the pilot would be advised to wait until such an occasion.

Landing calculations using similar tables follow the same procedure, however, remember to use the correct factor (1.43) to come to the net performance figure.

10.4 Graphs

Other Flight Manuals include graphs to calculate the various distances required. That below is similar to one published in a PA28 - 181 Flight Manual. Others differ slightly, but the principle is the same. As in the table at paragraph 10.2, lift off and initial climb speeds may be given.

25° Flaps Take-off Performance

Full throttle before brake release paved, level, dry runway.

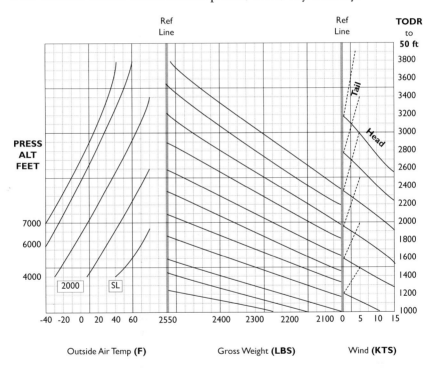

To use the graph, first find the environment details. If the temperature is 12°C (which equates to 54°F - the Flight Manual should give an easy conversion, but 0°C = 32°F, 10°C = 50°F, 20°C = 68°F and 9 F degrees = 5°C degrees), enter the graph from the bottom at that figure, drawing a line upwards until we reach the actual pressure altitude. Let us assume a pressure altitude of 500 feet.

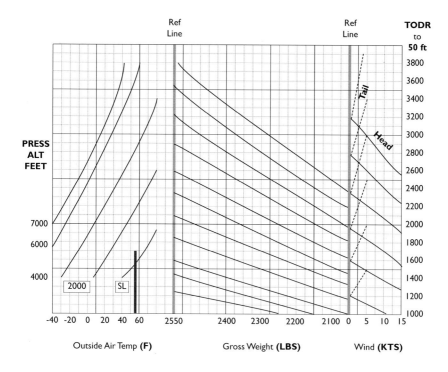

Ref Line   Ref Line   **TODR** to **50 ft**

PRESS
ALT
FEET

Outside Air Temp **(F)**   Gross Weight **(LBS)**   Wind **(KTS)**

Then draw a horizontal line across to the first "reference line". From the point where our calculation line meets the reference line, follow the direction of the nearest weight lines until we reach the calculated take-off weight. In our example, we shall use 2425 pounds.

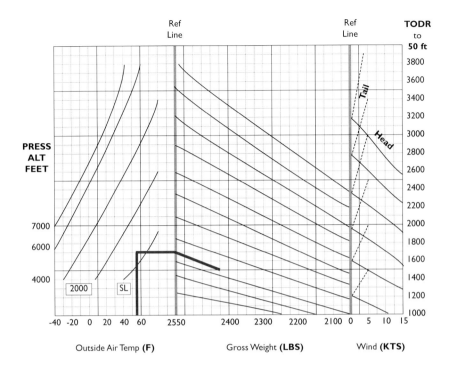

From that point, we must again draw a horizontal line to the next reference line. From that point, we must follow the direction of the nearest correct wind line until we reach the speed corresponding to the head or tail wind component (remembering to use 50% of a reported headwind and 150% of a tailwind). In our example, we shall assume a reported 10 knot headwind component, which means we use 5 knots.

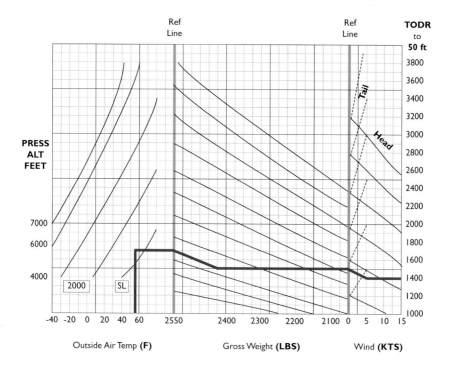

We can see that the TODR from the graph is 1400 feet. However, unless the Flight Manual tells us that the performance figures are already factored for net performance, we must multiply the figure we obtain from the graph by 1.33 to come to the final figure for the conditions specified, in this case 1400 x 1.33 = 1862 feet. If the runway slopes, or has a surface other than paved, we must factorise for these conditions using the table in chapter 8.

Remember that the figures only apply if the technique recommended in the graph and the relevant section of the Flight Manual is followed. Different graphs may cover different flap settings or different techniques, and may be provided for take-off run required as well as take-off distance required. Check that you use the correct graph and technique for the take-off you intend to make.

Once the calculations for required distances have been made, a comparison with the published distances available must be made, as in paragraph 10.3 above. Do not attempt to take-off if the available run and distances are less than those required!

Similar tables and graphs should be available for landing performance. Below is an example of one similar to that published for a PA28-181. The same system should be followed to come to the final assessment of landing distance required. Again check that the techniques and configuration equate to those you intend to use. However, remember to multiply by the correct factor (1.43 for landing), if not already applied, to come to the net landing performance figures required. Once the required figures have been calculated, compare them with the distances published as available, and do not attempt to land on a runway which is too short.

Gross Landing Performance

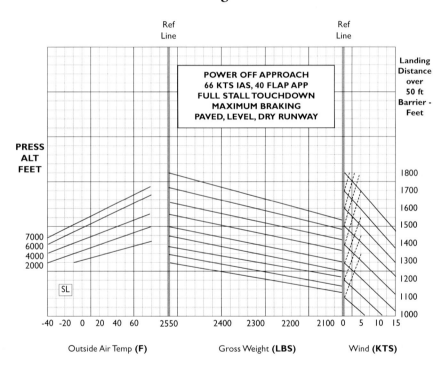

10.5 Exercise

Use the table below to answer questions 1 to 4. These figures are in feet, and for gross performance.

CONDITIONS:

Flaps 10°, Full Throttle Prior to Brake Release, Paved, Dry Runway, Zero Wind.

NOTES:

1. Short Field Technique as specified in Section 4 of the Flight Manual
2. Prior to take-off from fields above 3000 feet elevation, the mixture should be leaned to give maximum RPM at full throttle, static runup.
3. Decrease distances 10% for each 9 knots headwind. For operation with tailwinds up to 10 knots, increase distance by 10% for each 2 knots.
4. For operation on a dry, grass runway, increase distances by 15% of the "ground roll" figures

Weight lbs	Takeoff Speed KIAS		Press Alt Feet	0°C		10°C		20°C		30°C		40°C	
	Lift Off	50 ft		Grnd Roll	Total to clear 50 ft obst	Grnd Roll	Total to clear 50 ft obst	Grnd Roll	Total to clear 50 ft obst	Grnd Roll	Total to clear 50 ft obst	Grnd Roll	Total to clear 50 ft obst
1670	50	54	SL	640	1190	695	1290	755	1390	810	1495	875	1605
			1000	705	1310	765	1420	825	1530	890	1645	960	1770
			2000	775	1445	840	1565	910	1690	980	1820	1055	1960
			3000	855	1600	925	1730	1000	1870	1080	2020	1165	2185
			4000	940	1775	1020	1920	1100	2080	1190	2250	1285	2440
			5000	1040	1970	1125	2140	1215	2320	1315	2525	1420	2750

1. What is the take-off distance required with no wind, a pressure altitude of 1100 feet, temperature 15°C, on a dry paved runway with no slope?

   a. 1420 feet
   b. 1485 feet
   c. 1690 feet
   d. 2248 feet

2. What is the take-off run required if there is no wind, the pressure altitude is 200 feet, the temperature is 34°C, and the runway is dry and paved, with a 2% upslope?

   a. 960 feet
   b. 1056 feet
   c. 1277 feet
   d. 1405 feet

3. What is the take-off distance required if there is no wind, the pressure altitude is 550 feet, the temperature is 28°C, and the runway is short wet grass with no slope?

   a. 867 metres
   b. 1626 metres
   c. 2139 metres
   d. 2845 metres

4. If the pressure altitude is 450 feet, temperature -3°C, reported headwind component 19 knots, with a dry, level, grass runway, what will be the take-off run required?

   a. 635 feet
   b. 730 feet
   c. 938 feet
   d. 971 feet

Use the graph below to answer questions 5 to 8. The graph gives gross performance.

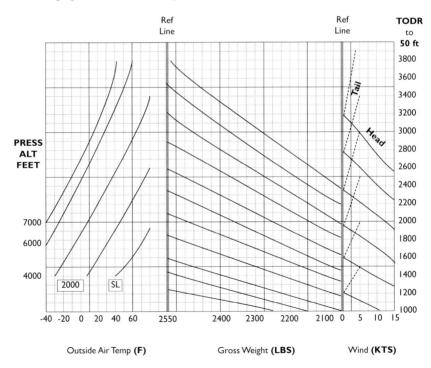

5. What is the TODR if the pressure altitude is 1000 feet, the temperature 80°F, the take-off weight 2550 lbs and a 10 knot reported headwind component on the level, paved runway?

    a. 2100 feet
    b. 2250 feet
    c. 2800 feet
    d. 3000 feet

6. What is the TORR if the temperature is 45°F, the aerodrome elevation is 400 feet amsl, the QNH is 1000 mb, take-off weight is 2400 lb, the runway is paved and slopes 1% upwards and there is a 5 knot reported tailwind?

    a. 1280 feet
    b. 1350 feet
    c. 1680 feet
    d. 1760 feet

7. What will be the take-off distance required if the temperature is 29°C, QNH is 988, runway is 27, wind is reported as 330/18, take-off weight is 2500 lb, the runway is dry grass, the threshold elevation is 300 feet, the far end of the runway has an elevation of 325 feet, and the TORA is 1250 feet?

8. What will be the take-off distance required if the temperature is 80°F, QNH is 1030, runway is 09, wind is reported as 060/15, take-off weight is 2350 lb, the runway is tarmac, the threshold elevation is 296 feet, the far end of the runway has an elevation of 336 feet, and the TORA is 500 metres?

Chapter 11

In Flight Performance

11.1 Introduction

Errors in take-off and landing calculations (or omitting to make them) may cause accidents, and have done frequently in the past. However, there are other calculations which the aircraft commander must make in order to make the flight safely. The aircraft must take-off with enough fuel to make the planned journey.

Fuel planning is especially important in light aeroplanes, because their fuel contents gauges are notoriously unreliable. Before take-off, the pilot should check the tanks visually, with a calibrated dipstick if possible, to be sure he knows how much is being carried.

Rules of thumb, such as "this aeroplane uses 20 litres per hour", only apply in specific circumstances. The way the pilot handles the engine, the propeller rpm, and the IAS he flies at, all contribute, as we shall see, to the actual fuel consumption. The same applies to any consumption graphs which may be published in the Flight Manual. However, the manual should also explain how to fly the aeroplane to achieve the published figures, and the pilot must follow these procedures.

Aeroplane in-flight performance as such is usually regarded as a branch of aerodynamics. However, because it affects pre-flight fuel planning, the JAR PPL examination includes questions on it, and the necessary theory is covered in this chapter, along with the more practical aspects of the subject.

11.2 The Balance of Forces

In chapter 8 we discussed aerodynamic forces. The total reaction (**R**) is split into lift and drag. In straight and level flight, lift (**L**) balances the weight (**W**) of the aircraft, and thrust (**T**) from the engine balances the drag (**D**), as in figure 11.1. If any force becomes greater than its balancing force, the aircraft will accelerate in the direction of the greater force. However, in this chapter we shall consider only steady flight conditions, not accelerations. In any stable condition of flight, the forces must balance.

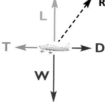

FIGURE 11.1 FORCES IN EQUILIBRIUM - STRAIGHT & LEVEL

In a climb, the forces must again balance. However, in this case the thrust acting along the aircraft's flightpath and the drag which it opposes will be inclined compared with the horizon. Lift, acting at 90° to the flight path, will also be inclined to the vertical. Weight, however, will continue to act vertically downwards towards the centre of the earth, as in the example shown in fig 11.2

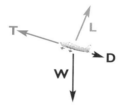

FIGURE 11.2 FORCES IN A CLIMB

When the aircraft is in a steady descent, the forces will again balance. In the case of a descent with power, all four forces will exist in balance. However, in a glide descent, whether deliberate or as a result of an engine failure, thrust will be non-existent, and the forces will appear as in the case shown in figure 11.3.

FIGURE 11.3 FORCES IN A GLIDE DESCENT

11.3 Lift and drag

As described in section 8.2, the reaction from the flow of the air meeting the wing produces the forces of lift and drag. For a given wing size and shape, the amount and direction of the reaction depends on the angle at which the air meets the wing and the airspeed (**IAS**). The proportions of lift and drag produced from the reaction are usually considered as individual 'coefficients' of lift (C_L) and drag (C_D), as described in textbooks on aerodynamics. The coefficient is actually the total amount of lift or drag force produced by the wing divided by the IAS.

It would be simple if we could think that the angle of reaction depends on the angle at which the airflow meets the wing (the "**angle of attack**"), and the size of the reaction depends on the IAS. That is true for the force which is referred to in different textbooks as either "induced drag", "parasite drag", or "lift-dependent drag". Unfortunately, the wings, and the rest of the aircraft, produce a certain amount of drag just because of their size and shape. This "profile drag", which car manufacturers also attempt to minimise, is zero when the aircraft is not moving, and increases as the square of the IAS. The total drag force affecting the aircraft is really the sum of these two totally separate drag forces. Having to include two different drag components complicates calculations, so graphs are usually drawn to show how lift and drag (or their coefficients) vary with either angle of attack or speed. These are shown in textbooks on aerodynamics or 'principles of flight', but this book is not specifically concerned with them.

Before continuing, however, we should remind ourselves of the graph of C_L against the angle of attack, shown in figure 11.4 below. The highest point of the graph is the point at which increasing the angle starts to cause a reduction in lift - the stalling or 'critical' angle.

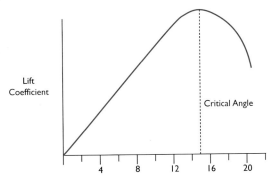

FIGURE 11.4 C_L CHANGING WITH ANGLE OF ATTACK

In straight and level flight, the amount of lift required is equal to the total weight of the aircraft. Since the lift developed by a given size and shape of wing depends directly on only two factors, the angle of attack and the indicated airspeed, it can be seen that at any particular speed, the wing must be at a certain angle of attack to provide the lift needed. The pilot would normally use his controls to select a pitch attitude which gives the correct angle of attack; this would be the straight and level attitude for that speed.. A low speed would require a high angle of attack and a high nose attitude, a high IAS requires a lower angle of attack and lower nose attitude.

From our graph at fig 11.4, reducing speed below the point when the critical angle is needed to maintain level flight would produce less lift than that required to balance the weight, and the aircraft would accelerate towards the ground. This is what we call the stall, and to return the aircraft to level flight we must reduce the angle of attack and increase speed, which the correct stall recovery technique will produce, but only after the aircraft has descended a certain amount. However, in that stalled condition, the aircraft is flying very inefficiently, and to obtain good performance from our aeroplane we need to fly efficiently.

The angle of attack which maintains straight and level flight produces a certain amount of **Induced drag**. At high speed and low angle of attack, the induced drag is low. At low speed and high angle, Induced drag is high. **Profile drag**, however, increases as the square of the IAS. Figure 11.5 shows the variation in the two drag components as IAS changes. Adding both drag components together, as shown in figure 11.5, produces a curve of **Total drag** which has a minimum at a certain airspeed (the minimum drag speed).

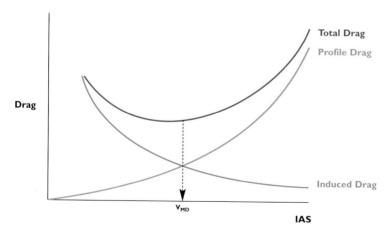

FIGURE 11.5   DRAG AGAINST IAS

If we fly the aircraft at that minimum drag IAS (shortened to V_{IMD} or V_{MD}), we shall achieve maximum efficiency (another way of saying maximum performance). When drag is at a minimum, so is the thrust required to counter that drag. If there is no thrust from the engine, for example in a glide, the speed which will give the greatest **range** (distance) in still air is the speed for minimum drag. In fact, the speed which will give the best angle of climb in still air is also the speed for minimum drag. Because the amount of lift required varies with weight, so does the induced drag, and therefore the total drag, so the speed for minimum drag reduces (slightly) as weight reduces.

A propeller driven aeroplane gets thrust from the action of the propeller on the air. The propeller may be designed to be most efficient at speed greater than minimum drag speed, so for best overall efficiency (maximum range) the ideal speed may be a compromise between the two. However, for examination purposes that will usually be ignored. Nevertheless, the fact that the propeller is most efficient in air with high density means that for best performance, a piston engined aeroplane should be flown at the lowest altitude which is safe.

11.4 Power and Endurance

The primary engine control is the throttle. Other controls may be available, which we shall consider later. Basically, the throttle controls the amount of fuel fed into the engine. The engine then converts the energy from that fuel into rotating energy, and the propeller converts that into power. Power is the rate of doing work, which itself is a force multiplied by the distance the force moves (force times distance), so power is the product of a force and a speed (thrust x TAS).

If a pilot just wants to stay airborne for as long as possible, perhaps waiting for some bad weather to pass his landing aerodrome, he wants to fly for maximum 'endurance', using the minimum amount of fuel. He needs to fly at the speed which requires the minimum power (drag x TAS). For simplicity, we shall consider sea level in the standard atmosphere where IAS = TAS. Multiplying drag by IAS from figure 11.5 gives a power required curve rather like that in figure 11.6. The speed for minimum **power** is less than that for minimum **drag** (which occurs at the point where the tangent from the origin meets the power required curve). The drag is a little greater at the lower speed, but since TAS is lower the product (drag x TAS) is lower than at V_{IMD}.

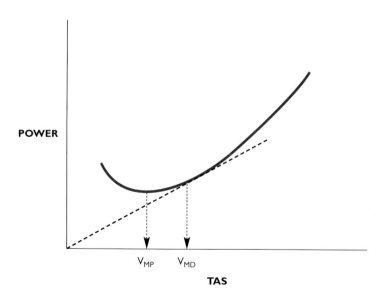

FIGURE 11.6 POWER REQUIRED AGAINST TAS

11.5 Cruising

Pilots seldom want to fly for the absolute maximum range. They are often content to use more fuel to get to their destination faster. However, in order not to waste fuel, they should try to minimise drag by flying in balance, with flaps (and undercarriage if applicable) up, and any other protuberances such as windows and engine cowl (cooling) flaps closed. Fuel consumption can also be reduced by leaning the mixture as recommended by the manufacturer, keeping the carburettor heat in the cold position (see para 11.10), selecting an efficient propeller rpm if applicable, and using any other techniques recommended in the Flight Manual.

For performance planning, they need to know how much fuel they will use during that cruise, so graphs or tables are provided in the Flight Manual, showing the fuel consumption and TAS obtained at different power settings. The pilot has no gauge to show power settings, so normally he selects an IAS, calculates the TAS, and reads the fuel consumption against that. Figure 11.7 shows a cruise performance table similar to that for a Cessna 172, which unlike some others, includes the expected rpm to achieve those figures. If for example we fly at a TAS of **102** knots (calculated from a navigation computer), at a pressure altitude of 4000 feet and a temperature of +7°C (which is the temperature expected at that altitude in the international standard atmosphere), power used would be **59%** with a fuel consumption of **6.6** US gallons per hour.

However, the Flight Manual figures are taken from flight tests of a new aircraft with a new engine. The CAA recommends that for older aeroplanes, pilots should expect to use about 20% more fuel than that calculated from the tables on page 90.

CRUISE PERFORMANCE

CONDITIONS: 2400 pounds auw, recommended lean mixture, speed fairings fitted. Without fairings, speed reduced by 2 kts

Press Alt (ft)	RPM	ISA - 20° C			ISA			ISA + 20° C		
		% BHP	KTAS	GPH	% BHP	KTAS	GPH	% BHP	KTAS	GPH
2000	2500	-	-	-	76	114	8.5	72	114	8.1
	2400	72	110	8.1	69	109	7.7	65	108	7.3
	2300	65	104	7.3	62	103	6.9	59	102	6.6
	2200	58	99	6.6	55	97	6.3	53	96	6.1
	2100	52	92	6.0	50	91	5.8	48	89	5.7
4000	2550	-	-	-	76	117	8.5	72	116	8.1
	2500	77	115	8.6	73	114	8.1	69	113	7.7
	2400	69	109	7.8	65	108	7.3	62	107	7.0
	2300	62	104	7.0	**59**	**102**	**6.6**	57	101	6.4
	2200	56	98	6.3	54	96	6.1	51	94	5.9
	2100	51	91	5.8	48	89	5.7	47	88	5.5
6000	2600	-	-	-	77	119	8.6	72	118	8.1
	2500	73	114	8.2	69	113	7.8	66	112	7.4
	2400	66	108	7.4	63	107	7.0	60	106	6.7
	2300	60	103	6.7	57	101	6.4	55	99	6.2
	2200	54	96	6.1	52	95	5.9	50	92	5.8
	2100	49	90	5.7	47	88	5.5	46	86	5.5
8000	2650	-	-	-	77	121	8.6	73	120	8.1
	2600	77	119	8.7	73	118	8.2	69	117	7.8
	2500	70	113	7.8	66	112	7.4	63	111	7.1
	2400	63	108	7.1	60	106	6.7	58	104	6.5
	2300	57	101	6.4	55	100	6.2	53	97	6.0
	2200	52	95	6.0	50	93	5.8	49	91	5.7

FIGURE 11.7   CRUISE PERFORMANCE TABLE

To use the above table, the pilot should interpolate the figures as required. As in previous tables, it is quicker and more practical to just select the next highest reading. In fact, it can be seen that the fuel consumption remains fairly constant with TAS at most temperatures and altitudes. This is often found in light aircraft.

In the table above, wheel (speed) fairings are quoted as fitted. These reduce profile drag, but are often removed for training. The TAS achieved at the various power settings without them would be reduced by 2 knots. To make calculations for an aeroplane without fairings, we would either need to interpolate the table for a TAS of 104 knots, or change our flight plan speeds by 2 knots.

To demonstrate interpolation, needed for accurate calculations, let us work through an example. Similar techniques may be required in other tables for examination purposes, or for airtest purposes to check the aircraft against the manufacturer's performance figures. Let us use an example of a TAS of 100 knots at a pressure altitude of 3000 feet and a temperature of +4°C. The temperature in the ISA at 3000 feet would be +9°C, so the temperature is ISA -5°, a quarter of the way between ISA and ISA -20. At 2000 feet ISA-20, 100 knots is $^1/_5$ of the way between **99** kt and **104** kt, so would be obtained at **2220** rpm at **59.2** (approx) % BHP (brake horse power - a unit of power) at a consumption of **6.75** gph.

CRUISE PERFORMANCE									
CONDITIONS: 2400 pounds auw, recommended lean mixture, speed fairings fitted. Without fairings, speed reduced by 2 kts									
Press Alt (ft)	RPM	ISA - 20° C			ISA			ISA + 20° C		
		% BHP	KTAS	GPH	% BHP	KTAS	GPH	% BHP	KTAS	GPH
2000	2500	-	-	-	76	114	8.5	72	114	8.1
	2400	72	110	8.1	69	109	7.7	65	108	7.3
	2300	**65**	**104**	**7.3**	62	103	6.9	59	102	6.6
	2200	**58**	**99**	**6.6**	55	97	6.3	53	96	6.1
	2100	52	92	6.0	50	91	5.8	48	89	5.7
4000	2550	-	-	-	76	117	8.5	72	116	8.1
	2500	77	115	8.6	73	114	8.1	69	113	7.7
	2400	69	109	7.8	65	108	7.3	62	107	7.0
	2300	62	104	7.0	**59**	**102**	**6.6**	57	101	6.4
	2200	56	98	6.3	54	96	6.1	51	94	5.9
	2100	51	91	5.8	48	89	5.7	47	88	5.5

At 4000 feet ISA-20, the rpm would be **2240**, BHP **58** (approx), and consumption **6.55** gph. Therefore at 3000 ft, the figures would be half way between the two, in other words 2230 rpm, 58.6% BHP, and 6.65 gph.

CRUISE PERFORMANCE

CONDITIONS: 2400 pounds auw, recommended lean mixture, speed fairings fitted. Without fairings, speed reduced by 2 kts

Press Alt (ft)	RPM	ISA - 20° C			ISA			ISA + 20° C		
		% BHP	KTAS	GPH	% BHP	KTAS	GPH	% BHP	KTAS	GPH
2000	2500	-	-	-	76	114	8.5	72	114	8.1
	2400	72	110	8.1	69	109	7.7	65	108	7.3
	2300	65	104	7.3	**62**	**103**	**6.9**	59	102	6.6
	2200	58	99	6.6	**55**	**97**	**6.3**	53	96	6.1
	2100	52	92	6.0	50	91	5.8	48	89	5.7
4000	2550	-	-	-	76	117	8.5	72	116	8.1
	2500	77	115	8.6	73	114	8.1	69	113	7.7
	2400	69	109	7.8	65	108	7.3	62	107	7.0
	2300	62	104	7.0	**59**	**102**	**6.6**	57	101	6.4
	2200	56	98	6.3	54	96	**6.1**	51	94	5.9
	2100	51	91	5.8	48	89	5.7	47	88	5.5

Working out the same calculations for ISA, at 2000 ft we find a rpm of **2250**, **58.5%** BHP, and **6.6** gph, and at 4000 ft, **2265** rpm, **57%** BHP, and **6.4** gph   (all approximate), so at 3000 ft the rpm should be 2257, at 57.7% BHP, and 6.5 gph. If we finish interpolation by taking a quarter of the way from the ISA figures to the ISA -20 figures, we end up with an rpm of almost 2250 at 57.9 % BHP giving a consumption of 6.54 US gallons per hour, which is the most important calculation.

Some manuals give figures for 'air nautical miles per gallon' of fuel, which are only useful in still air. Proper planning involves calculating time taken for each leg, and fuel used at the TAS to be flown. In the example above, a leg time of 25 minutes would use 6.54 x 25/60 = 2.725 US gallons.

11.6 Takeoff and Climb

We have already seen that the best angle of climb in still air is achieved at minimum drag speed. Short field take-offs use that figure to clear obstructions while climbing just after take-off. The actual angle depends on the wind, but handling requirements (avoiding the stall) normally dictate that the speed to fly for best angle of climb should remain the same.

However, in most cases, the angle of climb is immaterial after clearing obstructions. The **rate** of climb (how fast the aircraft gains altitude) is important. If we look at the power required (drag x TAS) curve again, and add the curve which shows the actual power achieved by the aircraft (thrust x TAS) we can see that there is an area where we have excess power available for the climb between the two points where the curves meet. The point where we have the **maximum excess power** (where the distance between the curves is greatest) indicates the speed which gives the maximum rate of climb.

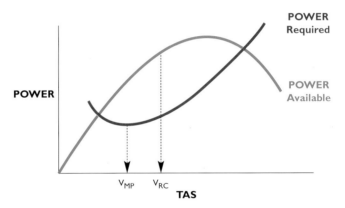

FIGURE 11.8 POWER AVAILABLE AND POWER REQUIRED

The power available reduces with altitude, and the curve changes shape as density reduces. The power required curve also changes shape, so the speed for best rate of climb **reduces with altitude**, as does the rate of climb itself.

The points where the curves meet indicate the maximum level flight airspeed at the particular altitude (on the right of the graph), and the theoretical minimum speed (on the left), although in most cases this theoretical minimum speed will fall below the level flight stalling speed.

Flight Manuals include graphs or tables for climb rate. These usually also include the airspeed at which the best rate occurs, as in the table at figure 11.9 below, similar to that for a Cessna 172. Any required figures may be obtained from the table.

CLIMB PERFORMANCE							
Weight pounds	Press Alt feet	Temp ° C	Climb IAS knots	Rate of climb feet/minute	From Sea Level		
					Minutes	Gallons used	nm(still air)
2400	S L	+15	76	700	0	0.0	0
	1000	+13	76	655	1	0.3	2
	2000	+11	75	610	3	0.6	4
	3000	+ 9	75	560	5	1.0	6
	4000	+ 7	74	515	7	1.4	9
	5000	+ 5	74	470	9	1.7	11
	6000	+ 3	73	425	11	2.2	14
	7000	+ 1	72	375	14	2.6	18
	8000	- 1	72	330	17	3.1	22
	9000	- 3	71	285	20	3.6	26
	10000	- 5	71	240	24	4.2	32

Based on Flaps up, Full throttle, ISA.
Increase time, distance & fuel by 10% for each 10° C above standard temperature
Lean mixture for best rpm above 3000 feet
Add 1.1 gallons for start up, taxi, and takeoff.

If the pressure altitude of the aerodrome at which the aircraft takes off is not sea level, the pilot should subtract the figures for that altitude from the total required. For example, if the pressure altitude of the aerodrome is 1000 feet, and the aircraft is climbing to flight level 50 (5000 feet pressure altitude), the time to climb will be (9-1 =) 8 minutes, and the fuel used will be (1.7 - 0.3 =) 1.4 gallons, plus 1.1 gallons for start up, taxi, and acceleration to climb speed (as described below the table) making 2.5 gallons total.

A similar calculation can be made to calculate time and fuel used in a climb from one cruising altitude to another. For example, a climb from the cruise at 1000 to 5000 feet would also take 8 minutes, and use 1.4 gallons. In this case, there would be no need to add the allowance for start - up, taxi and acceleration.

For climbs of 1500 feet or less, most pilots maintain their planned cruising speed, and just increase power to 'cruise climb'. The trim hardly changes, and the view forward from the cockpit is better at the higher speed, as is engine cooling. Figures are seldom given for fuel use during a cruise climb, but for short climbs the extra fuel used will be little more than that used in a normal climb.

11.7 Descent

Although many pilots will descend at normal cruising speed and with power applied, most manuals only give performance figures in a glide descent, which would use the minimum amount of fuel. The figures are also useful to calculate how far an aeroplane might travel if the engine had failed.

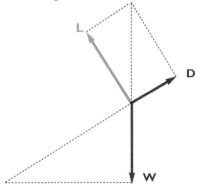

FIGURE 11.9 LIFT AND DRAG IN THE GLIDE

We saw the forces involved in a glide in figure 11.3. As can be seen from figure 11.9, the angle of descent relies on only two of the forces - lift and drag. The triangles formed by the lift, drag, and weight are 'similar' (the same shape with the same angles). That means the tangent of the angle of descent is the drag force divided by the lift force, but the ratio is usually turned upside down and called the lift/drag (L/D) ratio. Glider pilots use this as their main measure of performance. A glider with a lift/drag ratio (also called the glide angle) of 60 to 1 would travel approximately one nautical mile (6000 feet) for every hundred feet of height lost in the descent. Light aeroplanes may have a L/D ratio of about 6 to 1 (or usually better), giving a distance of one nautical mile for every thousand feet of height lost, although both these figures assume no wind effect.

At these fairly shallow angles of descent (1 in 6 is approximately 12 degrees), the lift required is almost equal to the lift in level flight (unlike the exaggerated figure 11.9) so the speed for best L/D (best gliding range) is effectively the same as the speed for minimum drag. The speed for minimum sink rate, or gliding endurance, is effectively the same as the speed for minimum power in level flight, although few light aircraft pilots will find a need for that.

Graphs and tables are often provided to allow pilots to calculate the point at which they should ideally begin their descent, and the fuel used during that descent. However, most light aeroplane calculations ignore the fuel saving in the descent, which would be flown at cruising speed.

So far, we have only considered the ratio between lift and drag. However, the resultant of these forces balances the aircraft's weight. An increase in weight requires more lift and more drag, ideally in the same ratio. That same ratio is achieved at a different airspeed - a higher weight requires a higher speed. The speed at which the aircraft descends will also increase, but the angle of descent will remain effectively the same. Flight Manuals often recommend different gliding speeds for different weights.

11.8 Practical Considerations

a. HANDLING

Flying at ideal speeds is difficult. For example, if the speed falls just below that for minimum power, the throttle must be opened to accelerate back to the correct speed, which means more fuel and less efficiency. Therefore, the speeds recommended in the Flight Manual will be usually be higher than those calculated as ideal.

b. WIND

We saw the effect of wind on runway performance earlier. When planning a climb, cruise, or descent, the effect of wind is considered in the navigation calculations. However, if truly maximum performance is required, it may be possible to vary the still air ideal speeds to achieve slightly better use of the available fuel.

Cruising with a tailwind will always produce a greater distance per litre of fuel than in still air, and gliding with a tailwind will take the aircraft further for a given start height, although the rate of descent (and the time taken for the descent) will not change. However, if the wind is strong, it may be advantageous to fly slower than V_{MD}, perhaps as low as V_{MP}, and 'float' along on the wind, staying in its effect, for both cruise and glide.

The reverse applies when flying into a headwind. At a higher speed, the wind has less time to affect the aircraft, so although more fuel may be consumed per hour, the total consumed to cover the same distance may be less at the higher speed. The same applies to gliding - gliding into a headwind should be at a higher airspeed. However, although the correct speed for a given head- or tail-wind can be found by manipulating the power curve, the theory is difficult to put into practice.

c. EMERGENCIES

Recommended speeds only apply under normal circumstances. Abnormal situations may require different techniques or speeds. For example, if an aeroplane suffers a fuel leak, it may be advisable to open the throttle and gain as much energy as possible before the engine runs out of fuel. The most efficient use of that fuel is probably a compromise between climbing and increasing speed, although weather will affect the pilot's actions.

11.9 Use of Flaps

Flaps change the shape of the wing, and the lift and drag obtained at a given speed. In aeroplanes, all flap settings increase drag, so in general performance is reduced when flap is selected. Climb rate and climb angle are reduced, fuel consumption in the cruise increases, and the angle of glide steepens.

However, flaps reduce the stalling speed, and change the pitch attitude of the aircraft for a given speed. For those reasons, there are occasions when flaps are advantageous. In poor visibility, a pilot may wish to fly slowly to maximise the time available to avoid another aircraft. Selecting a small amount of flap means he can fly slowly with a safe margin above the stall and still have a reasonable view over the nose. The same applies to a greater extent on the final approach, where full flap is normally selected for the main reasons given in chapter 9.

11.10 Ice

In an earlier chapter we considered the effect of a contaminated wing surface on runway performance. Dust, squashed insects or raindrops all affect the forces produced by the wing, increasing drag and reducing lift to a certain extent. Modern wing sections tend to be more affected by minor contamination than older ones.

However, the most serious effect on a wing is produced by ice. Any form of ice, including frost, changes the effective wing section and disturbs the flow of air across it. Drag from an ice covered wing increase dramatically. Lift is reduced and the weight of the aircraft also increases, requiring even more lift to compensate for it. The stalling speed increases considerably.

A pilot encountering ice should leave the icing conditions as quickly as possible. This may be achieved by turning back and leaving the cloud in which the ice has formed. Once ice has formed, it is difficult to remove, but descending into warmer air is normally the best course of action.

11.11 Carburettor Ice

Ice does not only form on the wing, nor only at air temperatures below zero Celsius. A major problem with aeroplane engines in typical United Kingdom flying weather is carburettor icing. Air entering an engine cools as it flows through the air intake, especially if that includes a carburettor venturi and throttle valve. If the air is moist, water will condense out of the air. If the cooling reduces air temperature in the venturi to freezing, ice will form, restricting the flow of air into the engine and consequently the power available.

Most aeroplane engines fitted with a carburettor have a heating system for it (fuel injected engines, without the venturi, are reckoned not to need one, although temperatures do drop in the intake system). Selecting carburettor heating normally brings air from the area of the engine exhaust and by-passes the air filter. The hot air reduces engine power output and increases fuel consumption, so heating is usually applied (fully) for about 20 seconds at intervals of about 10 minutes in the cruise, as a check for the presence of ice. In a simple engine, rpm will drop as heat is applied. When heat is removed, the rpm will rise again. If the rpm rises to a level greater than before the check, ice was present. In that case, heating must be maintained until it has melted. At descent power settings, the temperature drop at the venturi may be over 20 degrees C, so carburettor heating must be applied **before** reducing rpm for the descent.

Warm air can hold more water vapour than cold air, so if the air temperature is just below 20° C, severe carburettor icing is likely when the throttle butterfly is almost closed during a descent. A summer's day which combines such a temperature with moist air is the most dangerous time for the condition.

11.12 Exercise

1. In a glide descent, which force or forces balance the aircraft's weight?

   a. Lift
   b. Drag
   c. Lift and drag
   d. Lift, drag and thrust

2. A pilot flies the aircraft at the speed for minimum total drag. Which of the following will be achieved at that speed in still air?

   a. Maximum endurance
   b. Maximum angle of climb
   c. Minimum rate of descent in the glide
   d. None of the above

3. The speed for best rate of climb is . . . . . than the speed for best angle and . . . . . .with height.

   a. More,   increases
   b. More,   decreases
   c. Less,   increases
   d. Less,   decreases

Use the table below to answer questions 4 and 5. The fuel is measured in US gallons.

CRUISE PERFORMANCE									
CONDITIONS: 2400 pounds auw, recommended lean mixture, speed fairings fitted. Without fairings, speed reduced by 2 kts									
Press Alt (ft)	**RPM**	**ISA - 20° C**			**ISA**			**ISA + 20° C**		
		% BHP	KTAS	GPH	% BHP	KTAS	GPH	% BHP	KTAS	GPH
2000	2500	-	-	-	76	114	8.5	72	114	8.1
	2400	72	110	8.1	69	109	7.7	65	108	7.3
	2300	65	104	7.3	62	103	6.9	59	102	6.6
	2200	58	99	6.6	55	97	6.3	53	96	6.1
	2100	52	92	6.0	50	91	5.8	48	89	5.7
4000	2550	-	-	-	76	117	8.5	72	116	8.1
	2500	77	115	8.6	73	114	8.1	69	113	7.7
	2400	69	109	7.8	65	108	7.3	62	107	7.0
	2300	62	104	7.0	59	102	6.6	57	101	6.4
	2200	56	98	6.3	54	96	6.1	51	94	5.9
	2100	51	91	5.8	48	89	5.7	47	88	5.5

4. How much fuel will be used at 3000 feet for 30 minutes at 2200 rpm, temperature 9°C?

    a. 3.1 gallons
    b. 3.3 gallons
    c. 6.2 gallons
    d. 6.6 gallons

5. How much fuel will be used at 4000 feet for 40 minutes, TAS 103 knots, 16°C, no fairings?

    a. 4.5 litres
    b. 7 litres
    c. 17 litres
    d. 20 litres

Use the table below to answer questions 6 and 7.

CLIMB PERFORMANCE							
Weight pounds	**Press Alt feet**	**Temp ° C**	**Climb IAS knots**	**Rate of climb feet/minute**	**From Sea Level**		
					Minutes	**Gallons used**	**nm(still air)**
2400	S L	+15	76	700	0	0.0	0
	1000	+13	76	655	1	0.3	2
	2000	+11	75	610	3	0.6	4
	3000	+ 9	75	560	5	1.0	6
	4000	+ 7	74	515	7	1.4	9
	5000	+ 5	74	470	9	1.7	11
	6000	+ 3	73	425	11	2.2	14

Based on Flaps up, Full throttle, ISA.
Increase time, distance & fuel by 10% for each 10° C above standard temperature
Add 1.1 gallons for start up, taxi, and takeoff.

6. How much fuel will be used from start up to levelling at 6000 feet pressure altitude with a sea level temperature of +25°C?

    a. 2.2 gallons
    b. 2.4 gallons
    c. 3.3 gallons
    d. 3.5 gallons

7. The aircraft climbs from cruising at 2000 feet to 6000 feet. How long will it take, and how much fuel?

    a. 8 minutes,   2.7 gallons
    b. 8 minutes,   1.6 gallons
    c. 11 minutes,   2.2 gallons
    d. 11 minutes,   3.3 gallons

8. A pilot wishes to fly at the speed for maximum range in still air. At which of the following speeds is he recommended to fly?

    a. Minimum power speed
    b. Slightly above V_{MP}
    c. Minimum drag speed
    d. Slightly above V_{MD}

9. The maximum rate of climb is achieved at the airspeed when:

    a. power available equals power required
    b. drag is at a minimum
    c. power is at a minimum
    d. excess of power available over power required is maximum

10. Compared with flight without flap, flight with flap partially extended will:

    a. improve the lift/drag ratio
    b. decrease the rate of climb available
    c. increase the landing distance required
    d. reduce the drag at a given speed

Use the graph below to answer questions 11 and 12

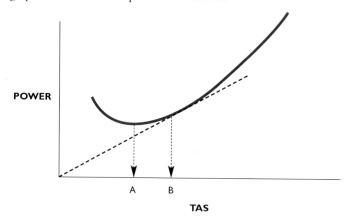

11. Which of the points indicates the speed for best angle of climb, and which the speed for best range?

    a. A and B
    b. B and A
    c. A and A
    d. B and B

12. Which of the points indicates the best endurance speed, and which the best gliding speed?

    a. A and B
    b. B and A
    c. A and A
    d. B and B

13. When gliding with a headwind, as against gliding with no wind, the distance covered over the ground will be . . . ., and the rate of descent will be . . . . ?

    a. greater,   less
    b. unchanged,   unchanged
    c. unchanged,   less
    d. greater,   unchanged

14. Ice on the wings in flight will cause:

    a. stalling at a lower IAS?
    b. some loss of lift but no change in drag?
    c. a considerable loss of lift and some increase in drag?
    d. no change in weight or position of centre of gravity?

15. Carburettor icing is more likely to occur:

    a. in winter than in summer?
    b. in the cruise than in the descent?
    c. when the throttle is closed than when it is open ?
    d. in dry air than in moist air?

Intentionally Left Blank

Answers to Exercises

Chapter 1

1. c
2. a
3. d
4. d
5. c
6. a
7. c
8. d

Chapter 2

1. d
2. c
3. b
4. a
5. c
6. d
7. c
8. b

Chapter 3

1. c
2. a

Chapter 4

I. LOADING FORM

Maximum Takeoff Mass Authorised: 2400 lb
Maximum Landing Mass Authorised: 2300 lb
Centre of Gravity Limits: 18 to 22 inches aft of datum

Item	Weight (lb)	Arm (in)	+ve moment	-ve moment
Basic Mass	1396	+ 28	+ 39088	
Crew & Front Passenger	330	- 6		- 1980
Oil (SG .8)	24	- 18		- 432
Rear Passengers	190	+ 24	+ 4560	
Baggage	70	+ 44	+ 3080	
Fuel (SG .72)	266.4	+ 20	+ 5328	
Total	2276.4		+ 52056	- 2412
			- 2412	
			+ 49644	

C of G position = **21.81**

2. a

3.   144 lb fuel =   + 2880
          4 lb oil =   -72
         148   + 2808

        2128.4 lb   landing 46836   =   22.005 in aft

4. Figures at (3)

5. **No**, the C of G position is too far aft.

6.   21.93 inches aft of datum.

Chapter 5

1.   44.44444 lb

2. Yes (moment change achieved is 1575 lb in, moment change required
is 1200 lb in)

3. c. Moment change required at takeoff = 12000 lb in
        Moment change required at landing = 12500 lb in
        Divide higher (12500) by 25 inches = **500 lb** - but answer is in kg!

4. No

Chapter 6

1. Total Mass **3911 lb**. C of G position = **52.28 in aft** of datum

Load Sheet

MTMA   3980 lb
MLMA   3600 lb
C of G position limits   42 to 52 inches aft of datum

Item	Weight (lb)	Moment (lb in)
Basic Mass	1896	80300
Pilot and Front Passenger	315	5500
First Row Passengers	340	19500
Second Row Passengers	60	31250
Baggage	60	32000
Fuel	960	25900
Total	3911	204450

2.   a
3.   3191 lb, + 57.96 lb in
4.   d
5.   Normal
6.   Utility
7.   d

Chapter 7	*Chapter 8*	*Chapter 9*
1. b	1. c	1. b
2. b	2. c	2. d
3. c	3. a	3. a
4. c	4. b	4. d
5. b	5. d	5. c
6. b	6. c	6. d
	7. d	7. a
	8. a	8. d
		9. b

Chapter 10

1. d   Round altitude & temp up gives 1690 but figures are gross
so multiply by 1.33

2. d   Round altitude & temperature up gives 960 but multiply
by CAA slope & safety factors = 960 x 1.1 x 1.3

3. a   1645 x 1.33 x 1.3 (CAA wet grass factor) x 0.3048
(converted into metres!)

4. d.   705 x 0.9 (10% off for 50% of reported headwind) x 1.15 (dry grass)
x 1.33 (net performance)

5. c

6. d   Pressure altitude is 400 + 30 x 13 (1013-1000) = 790 feet
Wind is 150% of 3 = 4.5 knots tail gives 1260 feet
1% upslope multiply by 1.05
multiply result by 1.33

7. 3700   Pressure altitude is 312 + 30 x 25 (1013-988) = 312 + 750 = 1062 feet
Temperature is 25°C = 77°F (68 + 9)
Reported wind component is 50% of 18 knots (60°off) = 9 headwind
Take 50% of reported headwind component = 4.5 headwind
Graph gives 2100 feet TODR, individuals will interpolate slightly differently,
     so ± 100 is acceptable
Slope is 25/1250 = 2% upwards, multiply by 1.1 = 2310
Surface is dry grass, multiply by 1.2 = 2772
Multiply by safety factor 1.33 = 3687

8. 2245   Pressure alt is 310 - 30 x 17 = 310 - 510 = -200 feet (take it as sea level)
Wind is 50% of 90% (30° off) of 15 = 6.75 knots headwind
Graph gives 1500 feet
Slope is 40/1640 (500 metres) = 2.44%
     so factorise by half that = 1.125 gives 1688
Factorise for net performance gives 1688 x 1.33

Chapter 11

1. c
2. b
3. b
4. a
5. c
6. d
7. b
8. d
9. d
10. b
11. d
12. a
13. d
14. c
15. c

Intentionally Left Blank

Index

T

U

W

Z

Intentionally Left Blank